THE OAKWOOD PRESS

One Dog and his Man

A 2001 Farming Diary

by

Keith Williams

THE OAKWOOD PRESS

© Oakwood Press & Keith Williams 2002

British Library Cataloguing in Publication Data
A Record for this book is available from the British Library
ISBN 0 85361 591 8

Typeset by Oakwood Graphics.
Repro by Ford Graphics, Ringwood, Hants.
Printed by Cambrian Printers Ltd, Aberystwyth,Ceredigion.

Acknowledgements

I should like to thank Tony Grenow for his cartoons, my wife Dilys and son Gareth for doing my work on the farm during my writing sessions, and Ginna Gow-Smith for typing my original manuscript.

Finally I would like to thank my faithful canine, Ben, for his inspiration and unstinting loyalty.

Keith Williams
Raglan
Mon.
June 2002

Published by The Oakwood Press (Usk), P.O. Box 13, Usk, Mon., NP15 1YS.
E-mail: oakwood-press@dial.pipex.com
Website: www.oakwood-press.dial.pipex.com

My name is Ben and I am quite a young dog of mixed parentage. My mother was a Jack Russell and my father a sheep dog. One of the advantages is that I am only of medium size and so do not bring so much mud into the house on my feet as if I were a sheep dog. However, one of the biggest disadvantages is that the pesky sheep can run faster than me, so I have to out-think them rather than outrun them. I live with my adoptive family on a mixed Welsh farm - Faulty Farm - close to the English borders.

The Gaffer – now he's something different. A great hulk of a bloke, built like John Wayne and with a Welsh accent like Tom Jones, but the bugger can't act or sing. Most of the time he's quite normal, but there are times when you wonder if the elevator reached the top layer. He wears a cap pulled down over his right eye and resting on his right ear. When he says jump you don't question it – you just ask how high.

The Missus – now she's quite the opposite, kind, considerate, a superb cook and she's the one who keeps the show on the road. Her only fault that I can see is that she's an awful judge of character or why else would she be landed with the Gaffer.

They have two daughters and one son, all in their twenties, none of whom live in the farmhouse. Sandra's in Banking, Tracey in hairdressing (she's in Australia backpacking at the moment) and she's my very best friend and always buys me presents. Gareth owns the Paper Shop in the village and lives in a flat above the shop. He opens the shop early in the morning and runs it until the first shift takes over, then he comes down the farm for the rest of the day. Gareth does most of the work on the farm now and so far does not show any of the undesirable qualities of his old man.

The Gaffer makes out he has got a bad neck and can't turn his head around to see who is behind him. I call him Pantomime Ted. Just like in the panto when all the kids shout out 'he's behind you, he's behind you'and the bloomin twit can't turn around to see.

However, he always takes me with him wherever he goes, in the Land Rover, the van, the tractors, the loader, etc. It's probably because I am the only one who will talk to him.

Note: The text that follows deals with the year 2001, the year of 'Foot & Mouth'.

January

It's the first day of a New Year and the Gaffer and I shoot out of the house in the early hours ready for milking and whatever else the day brings. I have to help him get the cows out of the cubicles ready to milk, then I go to help the Missus check the ewes in the lambing shed.

She's already in there and shouting excitedly, 'they've started, they've started'. The first lamb has arrived from our Pedigree sheep.

I go to check out this new-born lamb, and the ewe who only yesterday had been perfectly normal comes hurtling towards me at a high speed, fortunately I manage to jump on top of a hay rack just in time.

Up until now the two stock rams, Jim and Adam, and all of last year's ram lambs have been running with the ewes so now that lambing has started, they must be separated out.

After milking and feeding is finished these fellows are drafted out from the ewes. All of a sudden a shout from the Gaffer – 'Who left the B... gate open' as we see the rams disappear along the lane.

Gaffer onto the quad bike, I'm about to take my usual place on the platform in front of him – but oh, oh, see him putting on his goggles and realise this is no ordinary bike ride. Leap onto the platform behind him just as he accelerates out of the yard.

Faster and faster we go in hot pursuit, sheep two fields ahead, by now. Bike using a lot of fuel but not wearing the tyres out very much as we seem to spend half our time bouncing off the ground.

Closing on the sheep by now and going far too fast alongside an open ditch with a fence both sides and an open gate 200 yards away. I peer out from behind the Gaffer and am convinced he is going to leap over to the other side as if he was Steve McQueen in the film *The Great Escape* and getting over the border into Switzerland. I'm certainly glad I'm on the back seat so I land on top of the Gaffer not underneath him. The rams sense the futility of their planned escape and head quietly back to the farm to be taken to their new accommodation.

Everyone who comes into the farm shop now is asked: 'Do you want to see the lamb?' One fairly affluent couple and their two kids were wafting on about being vegetarians and how they were all extremely healthy and expected to live to a great age. The Gaffer told them all our sheep are vegetarians but a lot of them die young. He really is such a twit at times and makes you feel so embarrassed.

He says he really likes sheep but I do sometimes wonder. When anyone rings to ask if he wants to buy double-glazing he asks if they want to buy any sheep. They say they don't want to buy any sheep and he says he doesn't want to buy double-glazing, and he goes Baaa! as he puts the phone down.

Thank goodness for the January Sales and a few quid in your pocket from sales of Christmas turkeys. It's the television! The picture is so bad he's talking of getting a black and white licence to save money. The Gaffer's got very short arms and very deep pockets.

Off we go to the Sales – the Gaffer, Missus and myself. He really gives the Salespeople a hard time. They pick on the cheapest telly in the store and want discount, a free stand, free insurance – you name it, he asks for it. He did eventually get a pack of fuse wire worth 30p just to shut him up.

Got home with the telly, set it up, only to find the thing is really front heavy and wants to fall on its face. He's straight on the phone to the store complaining and they remind him there was a stand on offer that would have solved the problem and, no, he can't have the stand for nothing!

He goes outside and finds a brick and hangs it over the back and covers it with a sprig of Holly. What happens after the 12th Night I don't know!

What is your most sensational taste? Is it a chocolate that crumbles in your mouth? Or maybe the first bite into your favourite ice cream, or that tropical juice that conjures up thoughts of exotic places.

To me there can only be one truly great taste experience – that first taste of a rat. But you have to be really quick to kill the damn thing or he will bite you back. I then have to carry him around the yard for a few minutes to really savour the taste, and softness of its coat.

We are now cleaning out the turkey sheds to make more room for the sheep and in the last few days have had my fair share of that taste experience.

Our Integrated Administration & Control System (IACS) cheque arrived in the post today. This is the money we receive per acre for growing cereal and protein crops and also for the 10 per cent Set-aside which is compulsory to qualify. It may seem rather extravagant of the European Union (EU) to pay out all this money but with cereals at less than £60 per ton, it is absolutely essential for our survival.

One of the Gaffer's mates in England (I'm surprised he's got any mates) had his payment over two months ago, but here in Wales the Welsh Assembly are very reluctant to part with it even though they have been paid themselves. Every year they promise an improvement by the next year but it never happens.

We seem to be spending most of our time potato grading at present. There seems to be lorry or van loads going out most days and we also deliver ourselves to chip shops.

The majority of our spuds are sold in bags but a few also go in bulk or in boxes. The boxes or trailer loads are tipped into a hopper with a moving floor which feeds the grader. The Missus is on the grader picking off any bad spuds and there is a platform over the picking off table where I sit overseeing the whole operation. The Gaffer is putting on empty and taking off full bags from the weigher next to me, and Gareth is tying and stacking bags onto pallets.

When they speed up and start to get a sweat on the Gaffer takes his cap off and I can just manage to lick his bald head which is revolting, but seems to keep him amused.

We grow Maris Piper for the chip shops which are very vulnerable to changes in temperature. If the potatoes drop in temperature only very slightly due to the weather, they will not chip properly, and we are often putting heaters on them before grading to make certain we do not have a problem and have to replace them. I do wish the Gaffer would confer with me more often. We've been having a problem with the Bactoscan levels in the milk now for some time. These are high bug counts caused by poor cooling of the milk, poor cleaning of the pipes, dirty bulk tank and all sorts of other problems. With my very acute sense of smell it proved to be simply a matter of sniffing my way along all the pipes, jars, elbows, valves, jetters, bulk tank, etc. to find the problem.

About two weeks ago, we had a series of power cuts and the twit had not reset the timer on the water heater with the result that the hot water for the circulation cleaning of the pipes was not hot enough for thorough cleaning. This problem has now been corrected.

The dairy herd here is run on a relatively low cost, low output system to maximise use of the available quota. Silage is about 50 per cent grass and 50 per cent maize and is fed using a feeder wagon. Our own cereals and beans are used and are fed in the parlour.

The higher yielding cows are put to Friesian bulls using Artificial Insemination (AI) and the remainder are looked after by our Limousin bull, whose name is Malcolm. There are times when he really gets up my nose because he is so quiet and keeps following the Gaffer around. Because he is quite large he cannot lie in the cubicles properly and lies with his back half out in the muck which is quite disgusting, so he is put in an open shed at night with the dry cows.

Problem early this morning with a heifer trying to calve. Gaffer can't do any good on his own so off I go up to the shop in the village with the Missus so Gareth can help with calving the heifer before milking.

By the time we get to the shop, which opens at 6 am, Gareth has put most of the magazines in the newspapers and sorted out the papers that are ordered. The Missus is behind the counter serving, and I have a special stool that I sit on which is absolutely fabulous, as everyone talks to me and I am surrounded by bars of chocolate and all sorts of goodies that nearly makes me start to dribble.

Later on the school kids come in before they catch the bus, and one little twerp called me a rude name, which is a bit of a cheek. I'll remember him when he comes down the farm!

One of the girls starts in the shop at 8 o'clock so it's back down to Faulty Farm for the Missus and I. Gareth and the Gaffer had a nice Limousin bull calf to show me from the heifer.

Most Saturdays in the Winter the Gaffer and I load up three ton of spuds in the Land Rover and trailer and go and park in one of his selected selling spots. It's mostly in a lay-by next to a busy supermarket, and housing estate about 20 miles away.

We've been going there now for several years and they all know me and bring me little tit-bits to eat. I'll have to be careful or I will soon get as overweight as the Gaffer.

Some of the dogs who live up here think that milk just comes from the supermarkets. I consider it a vital part of my day to educate them otherwise.

He keeps getting letters and visits from the Local Authorities to move on but several years later he's still going there. I can't decide if it's his plea of insanity that does it or if he really does have friends in low places.

On the way home we stop at Rob the greengrocer's and he buys any spuds we still have on.

Just before we get home, and the old boy's feeling really happy with a few notes in his pocket, he starts singing. Well, you've never heard such a b...... row in all your life. How can a born and bred Welshman make a noise like a dawn chorus of crows? It's at times like this that I wish I had big ears like a spaniel to drown the row out.

Isn't it strange how in November and December you never see any magpies, nor any moles rising, but once you get into the New Year, the magpies appear and swoop down to pinch my food, and the moleheaps start to appear from the hedgerows. I don't mind the moles in the fields but when they start digging up the lawn I soon put a stop to them.

It's now coming to the middle of January and we have moved any stock off the fields that will be in Set-aside for this year. Ten per cent of our cereal, maize and bean acreage has to be left uncropped for most of the year to qualify for Arable Area Payments on the remaining acreage.

Because it was so very wet last Autumn, we did not get very much of our cereals planted. It's now too late to plant the Winter barley seed but we are still hopeful of planting several fields of wheat. The weather has been dry now for nearly two weeks and the Gaffer and I are cultivating up a field that we rose potatoes from last Autumn. We normally go straight in with the plough but have to cultivate first to level out some of the ruts.

I do wish that he wouldn't drive quite so fast over the rough ground. It's OK for him as he's got an air suspension seat – I hope the next tractor he buys has a cab with suspension on it.

It really is nice to be back doing some field work again after being rained off for several months, but within half an hour the inevitable happens – the dirty so-and-so starts breaking wind and he has the cheek to look at me as if I did it.

Gareth has now arrived to start ploughing, and 'Stan the Man' , our local contractor, appears with a tractor with combination power harrow/drill outfit to start planting immediately behind the plough in case the weather breaks again.

The ground is ploughing up a bit 'livery' as it's still not very dry so Stan has to go slower drilling than he would really like but the end result still looks really good. When he stops to fill the drill with seed I get on his tractor for a change. It's got really wide wheels on it so makes for a much smoother ride.

By this time, the Gaffer has finished cultivating and goes back to the farm to get the other plough. So now we have two tractors ploughing in front of the drill. The Gaffer is driving the tractor in front, thank goodness, or he would end up driving into the back of Gareth's if he stopped. What I can't understand is why some of the time he seems to be going at 3 mph and then 100 yards later he's doing 5 mph.

The weather is down to about –2°C by night and about +2°C by day. It means that the drill has to be caught right up with the ploughs at night or the furrows will be frozen solid by the morning. However, the following morning the ploughs will still get into the semi-frozen ground so we are managing to get in some fairly long days.

As well as planting Winter wheat, we are planting some Triticale. This is a cross between wheat and rye and is becoming more popular on marginal cereal growing land, and in our case performs much better than a second wheat with far less inputs. It is also slightly higher in protein than wheat so makes a better feed for our Christmas turkeys.

One of the problems of planting cereals at this time of year is that the damn crows are hungry, so at every fill of the drill I get off the tractor and chase them away but within 10 minutes of the tractor going they are feeding again.

Stan is much better company on the tractor than the Gaffer as he doesn't break wind, doesn't smoke and is quite a good singer with a better taste in music. However, the constant ringing of his mobile phone keeps waking me up. The Gaffer has got one of these mobile phones but he is too mean to use it, and hardly anyone phones him.

We've had our TB test on the cattle this month. The vet comes and injects on two sites on the animals' necks, and comes back three days later to measure which lump is the larger. We had no reactors but had one milking cow which was classified as an Inconclusive Reactor. She now has to be retested in six weeks' time, to see if she passes.

We have now drenched this cow with a Fluke and Worm Drench which apparently sometimes helps to go clear on the next test. The Ministry of Agriculture vets even sometimes recommend this action.

The incidence of TB in our area is a very real cause for concern and seems to be getting worse every year. Another cause of concern is the accuracy of the test itself.

When we are testing we do it through the cattle crush so my job is to help Gareth to get the cows into the crush. You just cannot believe how mucky I get.

Our telescopic loader is now over five years old and really needs changing. We've had a number of different machines on demonstration lately. We have some land and buildings where the spuds and corn are stored about five miles away from home so three or four times a week we have to bring loads back home either in boxes or in bulk. It used to be illegal to tow with these loaders but now they are classed as loaders rather than cranes it is perfectly legal. Also because they are about two tons heavier than an equivalent horsepower tractor they are much safer especially going down steep hills with an articulated trailor.

The first machine we had on demo would hardly tow a load at all, and also developed a fault so that one went back with a flea in its ear. The old feller likes to buy British if he possibly can, but after a wait of two months the only firm that makes a British tele-handler could not get the model we wanted here on demo so that one was ruled out.

The one we are favouring at the moment is made in Italy but has a Perkins engine with excellent visibility and the dealer right here in our village. In the end it will all come down to price. He could easily find a buyer privately for our old machine, but it is very hard to find a tidy, second-hand machine with low hours to buy for our own use.

The concrete on our farm yard is starting to break up in several places from all the weight going over it all the time. Rather than dig up holes all over the place in one go, and have a load of readymix, we have bought a load of sand and chipping and a few tons of cement and have stuck the old cement mixer on the back of a tractor and just do bits at a time.

The very first day I literally 'put my foot in it' – well all four feet in fact. The reason was a car with a dog in it came into the yard to buy a bag of spuds. I shot across the yard to sort out this flaming dog and, yes, straight through the newly laid concrete. The Gaffer was not very pleased so I thought it wise to make a hasty retreat and not to have too much more to do with laying concrete.

We've been growing Pick-Your-Own (PYO) crops here now for about 20 years, but it is not as busy as it used to be and the acreage has been gradually reduced over the years. We still grow strawberries, raspberries, blackcurrants as well as peas and beans for people to come and pick.

Pruning of blackcurrant bushes and the raspberry canes is normally done before Christmas but this year we are slightly later. We have a couple of guys come in to do this. With the blackcurrants some of the older wood and lower branches are cut off to improve the yield and make for a more erect bush to make the picking easier. All the old canes of the raspberries are cut off and the spawn that grew last year will be this year's fruiting canes. These new canes are then tied to the wires and all the old wood is carried away and burned.

I spend most of my time down the PYO field at the moment because of all the rabbits. I don't want to kill any of them but I don't half give them a chasing.

It's now nearing the end of January and over three-quarters of our flock of Pedigree sheep have lambed. The lambing percentage is barely 150 per cent (that means 15 lambs to every 10 ewes) which is about average for young ewes at this time of year. For anyone who has only ever lambed crossbred commercial ewes, if I were you I would stick to it. These Pedigree sheep seem to have their mothering ability and general livability almost completely bred out of them.

Even though the ewes are in excellent condition and the lambs born are of a good size the most important item of equipment you need is a stomach tube to get colostrum into its stomach as soon as possible. Normally if the lambs won't suck you put them to suck, but these little twits won't even suck half the time, and you must remember that the ram lambs will be worth several hundred pounds each in 18 months time.

For some unknown reason this year only about 40 per cent of the lambs are male which is a shame.

I've really been going short on my beauty sleep this last month as I have been up every night checking on the lambing. I overheard the Gaffer saying to somebody in the shop the other day that next year he is going to take the rams out from the ewes at night so that we only lamb in the daytime, but I suspect that was his funny sense of humour again.

Gareth has now had the Paper Shop in the village for nearly a year and one of the lines that sells really badly is paperback books so he has now dispensed with them and replaced them with something that is just out of this world – pet food.

You name it and it seems to be there – from tins with gravy, to dog mixes with cereals, peas, vegetables, etc. It is all so absolutely scrumptious. I can nearly smell it from half a mile away at the farm. Now when I am up the shop with the Missus, from my stool behind the counter I am looking straight at this blend of canine delicacies. All the time I am licking my lips to stop myself from dribbling and of course I am also chief taster and if anything is not quite up to expectations it is no longer stocked.

We also sell cat food which all seems to smell of fish or chicken, neither of which really appeals to me but is rather enjoyed by the farm cat. We only have one cat at present who is called Sooty. She is all one colour and spends all her time singing so I call her Shirley Bassey. She does catch the occasional mouse which is quite useful as it helps to take the pressure off me, but no way do I allow her near the house.

Today we are shearing last year's born rams which will be sold as yearlings this Autumn. The reason we shear them now is so that by the time they are sold they will look much bigger and we will have more growth of wool so that they can be trimmed up and their shape and appearance improved.

Gareth's best friend from school – Lewis – does the shearing and boy is he quick. He's one of these super fit and tough young farmers who inspires confidence in the youth of today. Lewis is also our main turkey killer at Christmas as only he, Gareth and the Gaffer have licences to kill the turkeys.

Now that the wool is off these guys they look a bit like a turkey that has been plucked. They will now have to be kept indoors until the Spring or they will end up catching pneumonia, but if the weather is OK we will let them out into the patch to give them exercise for a few hours each day.

There are a few of them that try to be really macho by standing up to me so I have to show my authority now or they will soon become a pain in the butt.

Gaffer and I are off in the Land Rover and cattle trailer today to look at some Pedigree ewe lambs for sale privately. As we drive up the Wye Valley towards Ross-on-Wye we are absolutely amazed at the amount of flood damage, this river land has been waterlogged several times so far this last three months. We also see fields of potatoes and sugar beet that are not yet lifted.

We arrive at the farm to find a pen full of ewe lambs that look really superb and are a credit to their owner. We pick out 30 to buy which seems to take a long time, but it's nothing compared to the time it takes the old feller to haggle over the price. This time he has really met his match and has to pay virtually the asking price but the quality really is excellent. One consolation of him having to dig deeper into his wallet is that on the way home he does not start singing which is absolute heaven.

After we get home and unload these sheep, he's straight on the phone to get some more ewe quota as he's cutting it pretty fine, date wise. You get paid so much per breeding ewe, or female over one year old, that are kept on your land for the 'Retention Period' of 100 days. At present this retention period starts on 4th February.

A number of years ago we had an official around so that we could become farm assured and all was going fine until we came to the spray store. This was built under a stairs and was too small and badly lit so it was suggested using another room for a spray store.

'Can't do that', says the Gaffer – 'during Turkey killing we do the heads and legs in there'. 'No problem' came the reply – 'take out the sprays wash the walls and floor and use it for your turkeys'. There was a long delay before the Gaffer answered, during which time his face became several shades redder. That guy never came back again.

There are ever so many farmers around here who have decided to get out of farming, especially if they do not have any family to succeed them. With the low prices of stock and of quota many tenant farmers are finding it difficult to even afford to buy a house. The owner occupiers are more fortunate, especially if there are old buildings that are suitable for residential development.

The price of land is completely out of proportion to its earning capacity – but our Taxation system means there are plenty of people with development money, or city money looking to invest.

What is most worrying now is the fact that the average age for a farmer is 58, and there are not enough new entrants coming into the industry to seize new opportunities of marketing, alternative crops (e.g. BIOMASS crops) and the farming industry in general is in severe decline. Most other countries besides ours have an Early Retirement Scheme and also a Scheme for New Entrants.

Most land that now comes up for rent is under a Farm Business Tenancy that is perhaps for only five or 10 years, which is too short anyway and the rents are exorbitant, and on top of that you may have to buy or lease in Quota.

The Quota prices for sheep, suckler cows and milk are probably lower now than they have been for several years but that is only because the commodity prices are so much lower anyway.

One of the Gaffer's favourite sayings is that 'things don't just happen, you have to make them happen'.

Years ago we were all advised to specialize. So if you had say a 100 acre farm, you should be milking 100 cows and nothing else but it is these guys who have been hardest hit by low prices as they have nothing else to fall back on. Perhaps we should be more self-sufficient by growing our own corn and peas or beans for feeding to our own stock, but if you are on a limited acreage, this is not possible.

In the Gaffer's younger days you were told to pick a wife with Wellington marks on her legs to help you out on the farm. Nowadays, you are better off to have someone who is qualified and can get a job off the farm. The down side of this is that if the wife is not actively involved in the farm, the sons are less likely to become interested in farming, so that in another generation there will be even less youngsters entering the industry.

At times like this one must think positive and be optimistic.

February

Already we are into the second month of the year and the days are getting longer (still only 24 hours but more hours of daylight). The temperature is slowly creeping up, the birds are singing, snowdrops in flower, buds on the daffodils and it seems the worst part of the winter is behind us.

It looks extremely unlikely now with only two months to go that the country is going to hit milk quota. Gaffer has just bought in a lorry load of concentrates for the cows, which is almost unheard of here as we normally feed a mix of our own cereals, beans and minerals. Some of the younger cows in the herd have never eaten any purchased feed before. However, it does have the desired effect of increasing the milk yield by about 10 per cent.

One of the problems of home mixing is palatability and also intake. We increase palatability by adding extra molasses and could increase intake by giving a midday feed but most years we are governed by our quota.

The quality of milk is much better when home mixing – both butterfat and protein are about .5 per cent higher which means you get paid more money but if your butterfat is up you end up using more of your quota which is calculated on your butterfat base. Some years we have used up a whole month's quota just because of high butterfat levels.

Our silage quality is quite poor this year. The maize silage was cut too soon as we wanted to get on with potato lifting. However, by the time it would have been fit to harvest, the field had been flooded twice.

The grass silage was of reasonable quality but because we had loads of potatoes unsold these were added in layers as the grass was put into the clamp. The potatoes had all been put over the cleaner to remove any excess soil and rubbish, but we really should have put them over the washer as well.

Gareth went to an National Farmers Union (NFU) meeting last night and the President, Mr Ben Gill, was speaking. We are right in the heart of 'Farmers For Action' territory where the farmers all seem to be very militant. I don't know if he expected a rough ride but he certainly got one. We couldn't decide if he was very brave or completely mad to attend. However, he stuck his ground and argued his point of view, but it may be some time before he next ventures to South East Wales.

It's only just over a month since Christmas and already we have to order our turkeys for next year. This is so that the hatcheries know how many eggs to hatch in what week number.

We used to have our poults as day-olds, but now have them at four weeks old by which time they are off heat and are so much easier to cope with. As day-olds they came when we were combining barley, potato lifting and still on the Pick-Your-Own, and time is at a premium.

One of the biggest problems with Christmas turkeys is getting the weights right for the customers, so we end up having four batches at weekly intervals and these are made up of three different breeds. They are nearly all hen birds with the exception of a few stags for heavier weights.

In recent years ever so many hatcheries have ceased to exist or amalgamated with another with the result that some breeds of turkey are no longer available. This year, we are having one breed that we have never had before so hope the weights at Christmas are as predicted. The price per bird this year is up 25p each, so the old boy is grizzling fairish.

Many potato growers in our patch are stopping growing due to the difficulties experienced harvesting and storing this last Autumn and Winter.

The three of us go to two different farms and end up buying another destoner at one, and a bed tiller at another.

We already have a destoner which is getting well worn, but the bed tiller is something we never had before, although we often had a contractor in with one. It certainly looks like a beast of a machine, I just hope our tractors can handle it on the steeper banks.

We're having several loads of fertilizer delivered at the moment which all now comes in half-ton bags and is so easy to unload. The Gaffer says it all used to be in 1 cwt bags which in later years were handled on pallets but in his younger days it was all handball work (i.e. by hand).

The price has increased by up to 40 per cent this year – especially on the nitrogen so I hope Gareth does most of the spreading as the Gaffer has been known to cause some awful striping. The b..... twit can't get it into his head that as the tramlines have got wider you cannot spread in such strong winds. He blames the spreader, but it's the spreader operator that is at fault.

Gaffer, Missus and myself went to Aberystwyth to visit some relations. I think the drive through mid Wales must be one of the most beautiful anywhere in the world. We went by the Royal Welsh Showground, through Rhayader and then over the mountains to Aberystwyth. We stopped at a café on the way and were really thrilled to see two pairs of red kite, which seem to be making a come-back.

It seems as if the mountains touch the skies and all is so peaceful. We came across some wind turbines that are used for generating electricity which must be so much safer than nuclear power. My only criticism of these turbines is their colour – if they were painted a different colour they would not be so obtrusive. The earlier models used to give off a constant humming noise but this is not so apparent nowadays.

Some of the farms are really isolated and you would really have to be brought up here to be used to it.

Compared to lowland farms, the overheads, especially of machinery, are minimal. A Land Rover and trailer, quad bike and a four-wheel-drive Zetor with a fore-end loader and bale spike are about all you need. One of the biggest revolutions on hill farms has been round bale silage so now you are not at the mercy of the weather. For about the last 20 years hay off the field has been £50-£55 per ton. The Gaffer can remember before that when hay often got over £100 per ton, as there was no real alternative for feeding the sheep or suckler cows.

Missus has quite a few calves on the bucket now. Mostly they are Limousin calves out of that dopey bull of ours (Malcolm), but there are also a few Friesian heifers.

We have also dehorned a batch of calves. It really worries me to see how close to the eye the anaesthetic has to be injected. I'm really glad that it's Gareth doing it and not his old man or I can see there would be a serious accident and we would have calves going around carrying a white stick. The toasted calf horn buds are a real canine delicacy as Gareth flicks them off the dehorning iron for me to eat.

The Missus is a great supporter of Farmers' Markets of which there are several in our area, and she always takes me along. While realising that these markets serve a very useful purpose, one cannot help but believe that they are somehow losing their way. Only about 50 per cent of the stallholders are bona-fide farmers and the rest have a small acreage but have employment outside of agriculture so do not really need the money in the way that the farmers do.

The average shopper will spend between £12 and £15 at these markets so if some is going on luxury goods produced by someone who often is not short of money, there is less going to the more deserving cases. However, the standard of all the goods on offer is truly outstanding.

The Gaffer grew up on a farm near Brecon and can remember going to the Produce Market with his mother when he was a young lad. The farmers' wives went to this market once a week with any surplus goods from the farm. Eggs, butter, apples, dressed poultry, potatoes, swedes, etc. Any money that was taken was then used to buy groceries and provisions for the family.

I can't really imagine the Gaffer as a young lad. Short trousers, braces (not belts in those days), shirt outside his trousers, cap on the back of his head, dinner down the front of his jacket. However, he still gets his dinner down the front of his jacket.

Most of the ewes with stronger lambs have been turned outside now that the weather is improving. The ewes are still fed some concentrate feed and the lambs have creep feed. This is fed in a long low hopper with a manger on each side and adjustable vertical bars that you slide back and fore. These bars are adjusted so that the lambs can put their heads in to feed but the ewes cannot get their heads in as they are too big.

After we combine the Winter barley in late July, we plant two or three fields with forage rape and this is grazed off *in situ* by the sheep. This rape is very cheap to grow and we also broadcast ½ cwt of barley as well so when it is grazed the sheep do not get so dirty in a wet winter.

If we get a surplus of rape we sometimes mow and round bale it for the cows. By planting barley with it, there is less likelihood of soil contamination in the bales. However, as the baling is usually done in late October, there is not really much chance of wilting so it is fed in conjunction with high dry matter, grass silage or maize.

With the current state of farming, there are an unprecedented number of people leaving the industry – 4,000 a year in Wales alone. The Gaffer says that tough times never last but tough people do. I hope that he manages to stick it out because the old boy is unemployable, and too damn thick to do anything else. He did spend three years in Agricultural College in his younger days but you would never believe it.

That Gareth really had one over on me today. Our dirty water from the run-off of the collecting yard and washings from the parlour is collected into a large concrete tank and pumped out to the fields by a series of pipes connected up to three sprinkler units. The Gaffer and I had been out in the field moving the sprinklers, and he had started walking back to the farm when Gareth turned the pump on.

Mostly you have enough time to get out of the way but not today. I got absolutely drenched by the foul smelling stuff. Needless to say some people found it highly amusing, but I did partly get my own back by shaking my coat off over them. I did have a hose-down in the parlour but that was really cold as you can imagine at this time of year.

The Gaffer is into vintage machinery. So far all he has got is a couple of tractors that are about 35 to 40 years old that he used to drive in his student days. He's also got a pick-up baler about 40 years old where the bales come out of the side which is quite rare, but is in perfect working order, and he sometimes takes it to vintage rallies.

If he's looking for a skive he goes tinkering with these machines but really he hasn't got a clue. He carries a small adjustable spanner in his pocket which is about the limit of his mechanical ability.

He's also a wannabe ploughman but really he's hopeless. He's got a few ploughs that he uses in matches but he never does any good. Either the wheel widths of the tractor are wrong or he's got the wrong points on his plough, there's always some excuse to make up for his own lack of ability. It might be better if he went a bit slower when he is actually ploughing!

We've had several fresh heifers calve and come into the milking herd just lately and really find it hard to believe how quiet they are.

It is now 30 years since the Gaffer quit working for other people and started farming on his own. He started milking cows straight away and at that time a good quality Black and White heifer cost about £200. However, out of a market of 30 to 40 cows there would always be at least two with a yellow cross on their rump and would be sold as not being guaranteed quiet to milk. These sold for about £150 and being short of money it was mainly these cows that he bought and some of them really were evil, but it was a case of 'needs must'.

He has his own yardstick for valuing a freshly calved B&W heifer which has applied for all of these 30 years. They should cost the same as 1,000 gallons of milk (4,500 litres). Our milk price at the moment is about 18p/litre and the better heifers are making in the region of £800. Two or three years ago when the milk prices were good, heifers were over £1,000 each. These figures also vary with the quota situation, weather, quality of silage, etc.

When milk quotas were introduced in 1984, we stopped milk recording as it was costing about £500 a year even then, and decided we would restart in a few years' time. Well, we still have not restarted. The Gaffer has said to Gareth we will restart as long as he does the two milkings a month when we are recording but he does not seem very keen. Perhaps we should do some kind of private recording, milk sampling to test if the cows are in calf and to test for high mastitis cell counts.

We have fine gauge milk screens in the milk line from each unit and can tell immediately if there is any mastitis present, and they both milk fairly quickly so avoiding any overmilking. They both say there is too much paperwork these days anyway and do not have time to deal with any more.

It must be remembered that total sales of milk off this farm are only 20 per cent of the total farm sales. If milk sales were greater, or even the only farm sales, then we would have to become more efficient. However, we are still managing to pay our bills so why change a system that works. More importantly, we are managing to do it without paying any full time staff.

One thing the old feller has very strong views about are business plans, and shuffling papers around. Once you bring in somebody else to start running your business he says the writing is on the wall.

About five years ago when milk quota was 80p plus per litre, even tenant farmers could borrow up to £50,000 (at an inflated rate of interest) off the banks. Some of these guys are now in serious trouble with quota at less than 20p a litre.

Whenever the Banks and the advisory services draw up a scheme to 'improve viability' you normally need to drop it like a hot potato and do the exact opposite.

The Missus came back from town today with some holiday brochures. I'm not really certain why, perhaps they just like to look at the pictures of far-away places and dream. Some of the accommodation now is just out of this world, and the old feller says he would really fancy a jacuzzi. I think the closest he will get to one of them is if he farts in the bath.

Some of the potatoes that we got out in the wet last Autumn still have some damp soil stuck to them and there is a small amount of mould growth on this soil. This is even after we blew air through them for ages. Normal cleaning and grading fails to remove enough of this soil so we have just invested in a Potato Dry Brusher. The intention is to remove this soil and also to put a shine on the skin of the potatoes. We already have a Potato Washer but less than 10 per cent of our customers want them washed, and also once they are washed you can see more blemishes and normally throw an extra 20 per cent away.

He located this Brusher on a farm near Worcester so off we both go with the flat trailer behind the Land Rover to pick it up. Going up the M50 and M5 we are amazed at the speed that some cars travel at. The performance of some is also staggering – 'will pass everything besides a petrol station' is his comment.

Get to the farm and they have a huge dog there so decide to stay in the cab. After much negotiation a deal is done, we load up and away from that yapping dog.

Just a few miles away call in to see the Gaffer's ex-employer, when he was an 18-year-old college student. They chat for ages about farming in the early 1960s and both seem to have a lot of respect for each other. It almost makes me believe that in those days the Gaffer may have had all his cups in the cupboard.

Our farm is not one of the tidiest but I would like to think that we are about average. We always have a good tidy up before the start of the PYO season, and also just before we start on the Christmas turkeys. It is just a pity that we let it revert back in the meantime. The Gaffer says that 'the Bank Paying-in Book is mightier than the Yard Brush'. There is nothing that looks better than a well kept farm and a neatly swept yard, but unfortunately they do not pay the bills.

Today is a very special day at Faulty Farm as Tracey, my very best friend in the whole world, arrives home from Australia. Tracey and Moose, her boyfriend, arrive back at Heathrow early this morning, after three months backpacking in Oz.

Sandra comes by early to collect the Missus and I to go and pick them up. I really am so excited to be seeing them again after all this time. Over the old Severn Bridge, which is really quiet these days, and shooting on down the M4. Sandra really does drive too fast, but there are even some cars going faster than we are.

By the time we get to Berkshire it is just coming daylight and a few miles east of Newbury I pass by what would be my ideal holiday destination. Hundreds and hundreds of acres of Christmas trees. When the Gaffer and I last travelled this way to the Smithfield Show they were cutting the trees ready for Christmas. What I would give for a week's all inclusive holiday, chasing rabbits and vermin in this heavenly canine adventure park.

The old feller knows this part of the world reasonably well as he used to manage a farm just south of Newbury in the late 1960s, and belonged to the

Young Farmers Club at Whitchurch. It really is a beautiful part of our wonderful country, and they still keep in touch with loads of people there.

As we get closer to London the motorway gets busier and busier, but it seems no time until we are at Heathrow Airport, Terminal Three. We find Tracey and Moose quite quickly and are they brown, I hardly recognise them. Lots of hugging and kissing, mainly for me, and off back down the M4 to South Wales. Some people say the best thing to come out of Wales is the M4, but I don't believe that for a moment.

They've brought me a present of a toy 'Tasmanian Devil' – it's an animal that looks like a cross between a dog and a pig and is found in large numbers in parts of Tasmania. It certainly looks a fearsome creature. They've also brought back a couple of Didgeridoos. The old boy will probably think it's an oversize pipe and will want to smoke them.

It was sad to hear on the radio this week of an Organic Farming Company that has gone bust. They were operating in the neighbouring county to us, employed a total of 35 people and had been going for 10 years.

Once a business gets too big to sell all its produce to smaller firms and ends up selling to the big supermarkets with their quality and seasonality standards and late (3 months +) payments, it can be very difficult. It's not turnover that really matters but leftover.

Drove past our local centre of Agricultural Excellence the other day and was appalled to see that all their fertilizer was stored outside without being sheeted. Hardly the best way to train our future farmers, especially with the current high price of fertilizer, the last thing you need is a lumpy, damp product for spreading.

The area in which we farm is mainly dairying with the exception of the marginal and less accessible farms. However, in the last 10 years a large number have switched to beef, sheep or let the grazing.

Traditionally any excess grass was grazed off with 'tack sheep' in the Winter. These would be either ewe lambs or in-lamb ewes from upland farms. They would arrive in October and the in-lamb ewes go home in mid to late February and ewe lambs in early April. They cleaned up any excess grass and were a valuable source of extra income. The Gaffer used to have them himself, but I've no idea how he rounded them up before I came along.

Now more and more of these tack sheep go across to Norfolk and neighbouring counties, where they live on vegetable by-products – carrots, potatoes, sugar beet tops, C Quota Sugar Beet, set-aside land etc.

They go across in the Autumn and stay until the middle of May and the grazier claims the Ewe Premium. It then only costs the sheep owner about £8 (which includes transport) for eight or nine months grazing which is less than they would be paying around here for only five or six months. Another plus from the sheep owner's point of view is that he is effectively reducing his stocking rate and can claim Extensification Payments. This is almost a return to the old Norfolk Four Course Rotation when roots were grown one year in four and grazed *in situ* by the stock.

Now the root crops are grown as a cash crop, and the stock eat the by-products. However, I imagine one would need to send fairly strong lambs there initially as I cannot see poorer, late born ones doing so well.

Gaffer had a few litres of silver paint left over from painting the wheels of his vintage tractors so decided to paint the stallwork in the milking parlour. You just cannot believe that anyone could even make a mess of a job like that. There seems to be more paint on the floor than on the stallwork – talk about Picasso. If that wasn't enough he dropped his pipe in the pot of paint and had to fish it out with his hand. Pipe grey, hand grey, paint grey, air blue – nothing changes. It took him longer to clean out his pipe than to paint all the stallwork. Talk about the Tin Man in the film *The Wizard of Oz*, I'm half expecting Judy Garland to come walking down the Yellow Brick Road.

Had one of our ewes today that had 'Ring-Womb' (cervix not dilated) and could not lamb. Tracey and I took it down to the vets and did not inject to dilate the cervix as it can often cause a tear, so decided to do a Caesarean Section instead. Cost £60 plus the cost of additional antibiotics and ended up with one dead lamb. However, she was only a four tooth ewe so maybe next year she will be OK. The old feller says you need a very thick skin and a very short memory to be a farmer.

One of our bigger turkey customers has decided to retire this year as a big new supermarket is opening 200 yards away from his butcher's shop. Rather than reduce the number of birds we do for Christmas we are looking for extra customers. If any of you are thinking of starting a Christmas turkey enterprise, my advice to you is not to bother, as it is an unbelievably difficult market to get into. If a butcher knows he can get the quality and weight of birds that he requires there is no way that he will change.

However, a few days before Christmas ever so many butchers may be short of 20 or so birds of a specific weight and it is these orders that we are looking for. The Gaffer and I spend several days going around butcher's shops and introducing ourselves and the results are quite encouraging. The last thing he wants to do is pinch other growers' customers but at the price he charges, he is unlikely to do that.

We also take bags of Maris Piper potatoes and drop into fish & chip shops looking for new customers. There is a whole range of goodies you can now have with your chips – fish, sausage, pies, pizza, kebabs, donner kebabs (lamb), etc., but never beef.

If restaurants can buy 8 oz. steaks then why not slice these into say four thin pieces and have them in a bun or something, it would help the beef sales. Come on you marketing gurus, there's an opportunity going begging here.

About six months ago Gareth got planning permission to build an extension to the back of his shop in the village. He's had a few quotes which seemed on the high side, so now that Tracey and Moose are home, Moose who is a builder, is going to do the work. First of all we have to demolish a lean-to and rebuild a garden wall before the building itself can be started. A trailer is parked in the car park outside and we are barrowing the rubbish onto it.

By sitting on an outside wall I can oversee the whole operation and still have the wonderful smell of the pet food from inside the shop. It really is so different from being down at the farm, and being moaned at by the Gaffer. We are also laying new carpet squares in the shop, but tend to do this after it has closed at 9 pm. Have also just invested in a security system.

We grow a small area of daffodils which should be out in flower by the end of the month. These will then be sold in the farm shop and in the shop in the village. The bulbs will then be lifted in late July for selling. A light dressing of compound fertilizer has just been applied to increase the size of the bulbs.

Several loads of seed potatoes are being delivered at the moment. These either come in one tonne bags or 25 kg bags and are tipped into potato boxes. Most of our seed comes from Scotland nowadays and the quality is really outstanding. In late July the Gaffer, Missus and I go up to Scotland for a few days to see these seed potatoes being grown, we never cease to be amazed at the hospitality of the growers and their love of good whisky.

The varieties we grow are Estima, Marfona, Maris Piper, Picasso and Desiree. Because our land is spread out into smaller blocks we are unable to irrigate at all and this partly determines the variety that we grow, and also the market requirements.

With the exception of the Estima, all the seed are graded 35-50 mm, the Estima 35-55 mm. The Estima are put over the grader – and any seed over 50 mm are cut in half by hand. This is an unbelievably boring job and quite slow – two of them can cut one ton between milkings. A small quantity of lime is sprinkled over the cut tubers to dry them up and stop any spread of disease. We have not found any reduction in yield by cutting and end up having seed to plant an extra 30 per cent of acres for little expense other than a few Band Aids when the twit cuts his hand. He does the same thing at turkey killing time so everyone tries to hide the knives from him.

At the moment I'm feeling as happy as a turkey on Boxing Day. Tracey does ever so much freelance hairdressing and she takes me with her. When we've got to go she always says 'let's shimmy Benny' which is a subtle difference from her old man's 'let's press on dog'. She puts a cushion on the passenger seat of her car so that I can see out and she also puts the seat belt on me and we just talk to each other non-stop.

Some people just have a wet cut, some a cut and blow dry and some have theirs coloured. Having it coloured takes hours so gives me a chance to see other people's houses and make new canine friends. I'm not too partial on the felines but some are OK.

Sandra and Carl live about 12 miles away from here and at the moment Sandra is going on several training courses with the Bank, and as Carl is away in London some weeks we end up having their dog over here. His name is Jake and he is a Labrador who is so laid back he nearly falls over. He is one of these highly bred, super obedient dogs and has been trained for retrieving game. By the time he's had a week here with me I've retrained him – or at least tried to. I just can't get him interested in any ratting at all, but if he hears any wild ducks or pheasants calling, he comes alive. I wonder if he has all of his marbles.

At home he sleeps outside in this luxury kennel but here he spends the night in one of the calf boxes. I certainly don't want him curled up on the sofa with me.

In this low effort, faster is better, age, everyone now wants all of the work done for them – potatoes washed, chipped, diced, mashed, etc. In the shop the other day we had run out of washed bakers and the Gaffer suggested to a customer that she took a few out of the bag she had just bought and wash them. I honestly believe she thought bakers were a different vegetable.

Some of the supermarkets are very naughty with the labelling of the potato varieties. Estima and Nadine are two of the most popular but the old feller has seen several different varieties sold under these names – the best one of all was a part-coloured variety (probably Picasso) sold as Estima. He got the manager out and made such a fuss that he discreetly took him to his office and placated him with a box of chocolates.

The Missus does quite a bit of label watching in supermarkets to see if they are not misusing the Little Red Tractor logo. Quite often they are but seem to wriggle out of it by blaming it on a staff error.

The Potato Brusher that we bought a few weeks ago is now up and running. We had to change the electric motor and also some sprockets to speed it up. The difference in appearance of the potatoes after brushing is really amazing and we have managed to pick up several extra customers. One disadvantage is if it is even slightly windy when we are grading, the amount of dust nearly chokes you.

After we planted the corn in the middle of January we had three weeks of very heavy rain and flooding so we are expecting there to be large areas of the seed that rotted in the ground. However, as we approach the last week of February, the weather has taken up with a succession of warm, dry sunny days with the occasional frost and fog at night.

This has given us the chance to spread muck on the land. The plus side of this is that quite often I manage to catch a rat. It's dead easy to catch the young ones but it's the big ones that are more difficult as they climb up the walls and escape, but not all of them.

Now that we are grading potatoes most days, we have loads of stock-feed potatoes. It never ceases to amaze me how many spuds the cows can eat each day without getting an upset stomach. Each one can quite happily eat 25 kg per day without ill effects. There are also potatoes from last year mixed in with the silage. These are completely flat and look like dried prunes. The cows push all the silage out of the way to find these spuds, so we have to fork it back several times a day.

Two or three mornings a week Gareth and I deliver loads of potatoes up the 'Heads of the Valleys' road to the west of us. It really is hard work on the Land Rover as at one stage it is all uphill for about four miles, so we do tend to use rather a lot of fuel. All of the people up the Valleys are very friendly and they feed me all sorts of goodies. In the last couple of decades the coal tips up the Valleys have been levelled and grassed over and large areas have been planted to trees so it is now a very pleasant place to visit.

One night a week Gareth and I go to Cardiff to the Cash and Carry to stock up on goodies for his shop. He faxes his order through in the morning and picks it up after 6 pm on the evenings that they stay open till late.

One night we were coming home late in the van from delivering potatoes to a chip shop in a not very desirable area and had the misfortune to have to stop at traffic lights. They are really quick up here and I was afraid we would have had the wheels pinched.

Six weeks ago when we had our TB Test of the cattle, we had one cow that was an inconclusive reactor. She has been retested this week and has gone clear so now we do not have another test for 12 months.

This last week has seen several confirmed cases of Foot & Mouth Disease in the UK with the result that all livestock Markets have been closed and stock movements banned.

The general public and Ramblers Association have all been very sensible and stopped venturing into the countryside. But talk about panic buying! Our potato sales have doubled in a week because of people stockpiling food which is quite unnecessary.

The Gaffer can remember the serious outbreak of Foot & Mouth Disease in 1967 when similar restrictions were imposed. There were over 2,000 confirmed cases in that outbreak so let's hope it doesn't get so bad this time.

In recent years there seems to have been a considerable increase in the number of buzzards. At this time of year we often see up to 10 or 12 of them standing in a field about 60-80 yards apart as if they are marking out their territory. They are mostly in a field that is in grassland. It's almost as if they have been sent by the Ministry of Agriculture, Fisheries & Food (MAFF) to measure the acreages.

Written on the wrapper of one chocolate bar we sell in the shop is 92 per cent fat free! This means it contains 8 per cent fat. Milk is really badly marketed and not many people now buy full fat milk even though it contains only 4 per cent fat.

The supermarkets have agreed to charge more for the milk they sell on condition this money is passed directly to the farmer, but would you believe it, the milk processors have pocketed nearly all of the money themselves, to add to their already vast yearly profits.

I get most of my outside farming information from listening to the radio in the mornings when I am in the milking parlour with the Gaffer.

It's been some time now since the dairy side of the farm went Farm Assured, but there were deductions for three whole months afterwards off our milk cheque. It took many irate phone calls off the old feller to persuade them to part with our money. Must be a computer fault was all that they would come up with. When it was eventually paid, no interest was added on for the use of our money. A very good scam if you can get away with it.

In a previous life, I think I must have been a machine operator because the louder, more complicated, more dangerous a machine the more I seem to enjoy it. Today for the first time this year out comes the lawn mower. The Gaffer or Gareth have to get it started and then the Missus and I do the mowing. Each time we get to the end of the lawn I get hold of one of the front wheels and drag the thing around ready for the next run, but sometimes I drag it around the wrong way and lose several brownie points.

It's about a month now since we started feeding purchased dairy concentrates to the milking cows in an effort to increase the milk yield. The yield went up by just over 10 per cent but the butterfat and protein dropped by more than .5 per cent with the result that the price per litre has dropped by 2.35p so we are actually slightly worse off than with home mixing, and we have a bill to pay every month. We still have plenty of our own cereals and beans left in store, so we are going back to home milling and mixing.

We have a mobile mill and mix to process our feed. They are a father and son team who each have their own machine and are extremely reliable and hard working. They suck the grain out of a trailer, the beans out of potato boxes and blow the mix either into the loft above the milking parlour or into hoppers for the calves, sheep, etc. They mill four or five tons per hour and the noise is really deafening to us canines with very acute hearing.

No matter whether it is the father or son who comes here milling, they nearly always bring along their Jack Russell. He's not very big but built like a brick outhouse and boy can he rat. His name is Ripper and once a fortnight for a few hours we really frighten the life out of the local rodents, and snuff the life out of many as well.

Now that Tracey is back from Australia I am subjected to health checks all over. She comes to the conclusion that my health has been sadly neglected in her absence. I need my toe nails clipped, have a bad tooth that is giving me hell, really need worming and it seems that I also have a number of passengers on my person, i.e. fleas.

When it comes to guarding my territory I will stand my ground against the most fearsome opponent, however the very mention of veterinary treatment reduces me to a quivering wreck.

First on the agenda is having my toe nails clipped - an appointment is made and Tracey takes me off to Colditz Veterinary Hospital. I have had occasion to frequent these premises previously and still retain vivid memories of mental torture.

The practicing vet today is a great tall guy they call Ally - him and I have crossed paths before and he still has the scars to prove it. I think Ally must be short for alligator as he has these enormous hands that hold you in a vice-like grip.

In an effort to escape I have decided to lull them into a false sense of security by pretending to be very docile and they then decide not to put one of those awful collars on me. These collars are shaped like an ice-cream cornet and stop you biting. Anyway just as they were gaining in confidence I make my move and snap out at anything within reach. 'Watch he doesn't bite anyone's hand', shouts Ally. It's not anyone's hand I'm after you dummy, it's your nuts I've got in mind.

It's taking three of them now to contain me, items crashing to the floor, they're trying to put this damn collar on me and I hear that Ally say 'inject him quickly'. This needle must have been the size of a buckrake tine by the pain it caused. I don't remember much more until I wake up and start to gradually come around. My toe nails have all been clipped and feel much better - I glance down to see if no other parts of me have been tampered with; thankfully I am still intact.

That Ally is standing next to the bed I am lying on, facing me and I'm thinking to myself 'Fruit and Nuts', 'Whole Nuts', 'Hazel Nuts', boy, would I like to change you from baritone to soprano in one clamp of my jaws. He had the audacity to say 'nasty bit of work, isn't he'. With that I lunged forward, jaws apart; the yell he gave could be heard halfway down the street and I just held on to him for dear life.

By the time Tracey returns to pick me up peace has descended on Colditz Veterinary Hospital. She comments to the Alligator that he looks pale and stressed and had I behaved myself? 'Piece of cake really, piece of cake', he says. I'm thinking to myself - piece of your trousers mate with your nuts in them.

Cough now buddy - careful! Some people pay a fortune for family planning; just a bit more pressure from me and yours would have been for free. On reflection as driving home I'm thinking of the latest confrontation in marks out of 10. I reckon 8 for me and 2 for the opposition. I must be careful from now on as the Alligator is bound to be intent on retaliation. I'm glad I'm not a bar mitzvah boy or it could just be a case of one stroke too far, and my reproduction chances scuppered.

We are now into the third week of the Foot and Mouth epidemic and so far 40 cases have been confirmed and all have a direct link with the initial outbreak.

We have a pad of disinfected straw at the yard gate for all vehicles to drive over, a disinfectant bath to dip one's feet in and any lorries vans, etc. that collect potatoes have their wheels thoroughly sprayed on entering and leaving the farm.

All ancillary services have responded amazingly well with reps doing their business over the phone rather than farm visits and any non-essential services and deliveries have been cancelled. The mail is put in a box at the yard gate, and hardly anyone now comes to the farm to buy their potatoes, they buy them from Gareth's shop in the village instead.

We are not in an infected area ourselves but the nearest outbreak is less than 20 miles away and everyone is being extra vigilant in checking their stock. In the event of an outbreak on your farm, all cattle, sheep and pigs are slaughtered and are burned on the premises and you are not allowed to restock for six months.

Compensation is paid for the animals that are destroyed. No consequential loss is paid so you have no income off stock for six months and the compensation is not adequate to restock fully. For the majority of farmers an outbreak of Foot and Mouth disease would all but bankrupt them if they were mainly stock farmers. As it is over 30 years since the last major outbreak in the UK, very few people now have insurance to cover themselves.

All public footpaths have been closed to walkers, horse racing cancelled, the Countryside March in London scheduled for 18th March is cancelled, as was the Wales v. Ireland Rugby Match last weekend.

As is usual with any catastrophe, all the experts are ready to apportion the blame. The farmers for factory farming, the supermarkets for having agriculture in an armlock (Tony Blair's quote), the Government for allowing inferior foreign foods to enter the UK.

The fact is, however unpalatable it may be, that it is the public's desire for cheaper food that is causing the present problems. Farmers must now produce food at a price the market will bear, and this is determined by what customers are willing to pay. Listeria in cheese, salmonella in eggs, BSE, Swine Fever and now Foot and Mouth have all been blamed on corner cutting to save money.

The problem is the public seem reluctant to spend more on food. A supermarket chain which decided to specialise in organic food started losing money. Other supermarkets have 'value lines' of cheap, flavoured, heavily processed foods which are bought in ever increasing quantities.

Only 13 Labour MPs turned up this week for a debate on the Foot and Mouth crisis. Did the other 400 think it wasn't important? Worcester Labour MP Michael Foster, concerned for animal welfare when he tried to introduce the Fox Hunting Bill did not turn up for the Foot and Mouth debate – talk about cynical self promotion.

What people forget is how traumatic Foot and Mouth is to us animals. Personally being a canine I will not be shot, but my movements are severely restricted because the Gaffer doesn't go anywhere unless it is absolutely essential and also very few customers come to the farm shop so I am meeting far less people.

Our two stock rams (Jim and Adam), the recently purchased ewe lambs and some dry ewes are grazing on some land a few miles away from home and at present we are not allowed to move them. I had a long chat with Jim the other day and it was just questions, questions.

Why are they shut on the same field when there is plenty of grass on a field over the road? Why doesn't he see cattle lorries moving tack sheep back to the upland farms? Why doesn't he see Land Rovers and trailers moving stock to Markets? Why has the Gaffer brought a hay-rack filled with dry unpalatable hay when we should be grazing fresh grass?

To save them further anxiety I do not say anything about the real reasons, but try to reassure them it is for their own and all other animals' benefit.

We've started spreading fertilizer on some of the grass fields to ensure some earlier grazing, but are only putting on a small amount. The down side is that it's the Gaffer who's doing it so we'll probably have the usual zebra effects (striping). He always takes me along and I am amazed at the number of rabbits that we have. Certainly far more than at this time last year.

Another pest that is increasing at an alarming rate are corvines (crows, rooks, etc.). Five years ago what was a rookery of about 10 nests now numbers over 40 and seems to be increasing every year. It seems as if the crows are building their nests alongside the rooks for added protection.

'Come on Benny, let's shimmy'. It's Tracey calling me. Now that we are building the extension up at the shop, we are off to builders' merchants several times a week. Out with the knapsack sprayer to disinfect the wheels of the van and it's away we go. Some of these builders' merchants are absolutely huge. We load up with cement, timber, pipes, ties, lintels and whatever and it's back to the shop in the village. Sand, chippings and concrete blocks, etc. we have delivered. The van is my favourite vehicle of all because I can sit in the seat and see out properly, without having to stretch my neck.

The second field down from the farmhouse is quite low lying and for the best part of this last winter has an area of standing water on it. Well, about three or four times a week I see a heron there. It's certainly not likely to catch any fish so we are hoping that it may build a nest nearby.

The Authorities on the Channel Island of Jersey are so concerned about the declining sparrow population that they are to impose fines of up to £2,000 on anyone who disturbs the nest of one. We still seem to have an abundance here at Faulty Farm, but this year I have not seen many flocks of starlings, which used to be very common at this time of year.

Two men are going across a field in a Land Rover when they spot some good looking pheasants and a naked woman. The chap looking at the pheasants has some difficulty pointing them out to his friend who is looking at the nude woman.

This, of course, is Prime Minister Tony Blair's problem. He doesn't know whether to pander to the allure of Labour's back bench anti-hunt MPs, a number of whom are members of the fairer sex, in the knowledge that a ban on hunting could ultimately lead to a huge loss of popularity, or keep his eye on the countryside. It is a difficult problem. Labour's hatred of those who hunt is deeply ingrained, it is a vestige of old Labour.

On the other side of the coin we have many field sportsmen who are natural Labour voters, but they will not vote Labour this time because there is little to choose between the parties, and their sport and the desire to be masters of their own destiny are the factors that motivate them.

If the politicians who are determined to ban foxhunting really think they can tell followers of rural pursuits to forget it, then they want their heads tested. Any hunting ban will affect all country sports. Any Bill to ban hunting with us canines will hit a far wider target than simply traditional hunts.

Animal rights campaigners claim only to want to ban mounted hunting with hounds, but producing a law that achieves only this is nearly impossible. Hunting with dogs can be classed as recreation and necessity, i.e. because they enjoy it, or for providing pest control.

It looks likely that we will be able to kill rabbits but not hares. I really hope that we will still be allowed to kill rats or else life would just not be worth living.

This whole hunting ban seems to be based more on prejudice rather than common sense, so why can't they just let us country folk maintain the correct balance of nature as we have done for thousands of years. I'll bet these animal rights campaigners don't look at the labels on the food they buy to see if it is produced in third world countries where young children work all day for a pittance.

About six months ago we were granted planning permission to convert some disused buildings and milking parlour on our off-lying farm into four holiday lets. We were going to commence work this Spring but have decided to wait and review the situation in six months' time.

Because of the atrocious weather of last year, and the strength of the pound, more and more people are going to travel abroad. With the latest Foot and Mouth epidemic, less people are venturing into the Countryside. The real reason is probably that the old feller hasn't got any spare money with the current state of farming. However, the Gaffer is a wannabe builder so next Winter I can see us both spending a few months up there with a trowel apiece.

The Gaffer's nephew, Andrew, who's in farming, often comes down on a Saturday to repair the kit that his uncle breaks and bends in the week. Give Andrew a welder and angle grinder and he seems able to make or repair most things, he certainly doesn't inherit any of his ability from the Gaffer. Last Saturday it was the turn of the farm van, which is well past its sell-by date, for a face-lift. The bottom of the back doors had quite a bit of rust, but some emery cloth, filler and a can of spray seem to have transformed it into something more respectable, if only temporarily.

Our new toy arrived this week – a new telescopic, four-wheel steer loader. It is fitted with a Matbro carriage so we don't have to change the brackets on all the attachments. It seems to cope very well with the work and also it does not have bald tyres like the old one so we can venture into the fields for the first time this Winter. More importantly there is a place for me to sit on the right-hand side of the seat which is much more comfortable than sitting on the floor, and I get a better view of what is going on. The old machine has not been traded in, but has been sold privately so we are keeping it for a couple of weeks in case of any problems.

Last Autumn we bought some old killing ewes to be fattened up and sold in February or March. Because of the Foot and Mouth (F&M) restrictions, we still have them on the off-lying land. That flaming ram Jim broke into them for a few days back in October so they have started lambing which is a bit of a pain as they are five miles away, so we spend quite a bit of time back and fore to check them. However, the weather is quite mild and they are much easier to manage than the pedigree flock.

It's Saturday 10th March and we have been served with a Form D Notice by the Ministry of Agriculture because our neighbour has a suspected case of Foot and Mouth Disease. This notice applies to any farm within 3 km of the suspected outbreak. It means we need a special licence from our milk purchaser to collect the milk, we cannot sell any hay or straw, every vehicle must be sprayed on leaving and entering our farm, and any non-essential journeys are strongly discouraged.

There are now over 150 confirmed cases of F&M in the UK with in excess of 100,000 animals already slaughtered. Livestock markets are all closed, there are no movements of livestock allowed – even across a road to the rest of your farm. Stock can go direct to slaughter (under licence) if you are not in an infected area. Farmers are being paid 20 per cent less for these animals yet at the other end of the scale supermarkets are charging 30-40 per cent more.

It appears most likely that infected material from South Africa is responsible for this latest outbreak, so a serious look at food import policy must be right at the top of the agenda.

There was a case in the press this week of a farmer who had insured with the same company against Foot and Mouth disease for 30 years and was denied policy renewal because of 'exceptional circumstances'.

At last we've got our quad bike repaired and back in action. His excuse was that we've been waiting for parts but I would suspect it's because he couldn't afford to pay for them. Parts of the off-lying land where the old ewes are lambing is really quite steep and wet and for the last week or so we had to walk around them. I normally sit on the front carrier enjoying the view but really it is much safer on the back.

We notice the birds carrying bits of twig and wool to build their nests and at nearly every pond wild ducks have appeared ready to breed. When you disturb them and they take off they make an awful row which really startles me.

We are now selling daffodils in the shop in the village, and many of these grow alongside the buildings and road so Macho Man picks them every day. He's such a twit that I have to stand guard and warn him if a car is coming so he can hide them in a feed bag.

In last week's budget which really was a pretty tame one, there was no mention of a pesticide tax which had been threatened, and there was also a 20 per cent reduction in the duty rate on Bio-Diesel so maybe we can follow the lead of some of our European neighbours and use up some of the surplus rape oil that is grown. Our vehicles may smell like a fish and chip shop, but if it is more environmentally friendly, it has to be good news.

We constantly hear of the contribution farming makes to greenhouse gas emissions and global warming by how much methane gas is generated by the digestive system of each animal. It is therefore refreshing to read of research that has been carried out into the freebies that farmers give to society. Tasks such as cutting hedges, maintaining stone walls, planting areas of woodland, creating ponds and so on. These are normally done by farmers in the normal course of running their farms and funded from their own resources. These work out on average to £1,400 per farm. At a time when the average income per farm has dropped to £5,000 per year, this is a truly remarkable contribution.

An away day today. Gareth, Tracey and myself go up to the NEC at Birmingham to a retail Shopkeepers Exhibition. Absolutely fabulous Show with loads of items that relate directly to our shop in the village – cash machines, security, scratch cards, shelving, new suppliers, etc. The biggest problem really affecting small shopkeepers is of course the large supermarkets with their strong buying power and free parking.

With footpaths, bridleways and fields off-limits to the public, doggie frustration is becoming a real problem due to lack of 'walkies'. Some of these daft animal shrinks are saying keeping a dog's mind active is as important as its body. They say that by giving us something tough to chew for a few hours will compensate for lack of exercise as long as our calorie intake is reduced as well. An obstacle course in the back garden with plenty of items to play with or retrieve would also help.

What we really miss about going on our daily walks are all the wonderful smells, and also the chat we have with other dogs, but until the Foot and Mouth epidemic is brought under control, we must all do our bit to help contain it. Some of my canine mates in the village say that if it continues for much longer, they will end up as 'mad as a bag of frogs'.

We have now had delivery of all our seed potatoes. Some of the lorries that deliver them have up to five collections in Scotland and then perhaps up to five deliveries in the South of the Country. I wonder why not on one lorry have all the potatoes for one farm delivery. In our case we grow five varieties and have had five separate deliveries. These could all have come on just two or perhaps three lorry loads.

It is now 14th March and about 20 new cases of Foot and Mouth disease are being confirmed every day with the total now just over 200. The disease this time has predominantly been in sheep – the most extensively farmed animal. They graze on grass, roam the hills and moors and are only brought home for lambing, shearing, dipping, etc.

Pigs on the other hand are our most intensively farmed animal. It is also the most infectious for Foot and Mouth. Yet except for the first case and a few isolated cases since, they have escaped. Why? The pig farmers are more aware of the disease and take continued care to cut down the risk of infection coming to their farm.

You can't by law bring pigs onto your farm till three weeks have passed since the last time you brought pigs in. This well tried safety net that has worked for the pig industry is not really viable for extensively farmed animals. This does, however, scotch the opinion that some of this last outbreak is due to intensively farmed animals. This disease was brought in from abroad and this is where the controls should be centred.

One of the problems with a catastrophe of this magnitude is being able to dispose of the carcasses quickly enough before they start to decompose. As is usual in the UK, 'the Government dithers while the Countryside burns'. Many carcasses are now being transported to incinerators and there is talk of the Army being drafted in to help.

Thousands of tack sheep are still on the lowland farms and have started lambing, with little or no shelter, feed or experienced lambers, which is really an animal welfare issue. The prospect of slaughtering the half a million sheep which are away from their home farms on tack – which seemed so bizarre when floated by Agriculture Minister Nick Brown only a few days ago – may have to be taken very seriously indeed.

MAFF vets believe that Foot and Mouth is more widespread in the national sheep flock than anyone could have imagined. They believe sheep are more likely to develop active symptoms if stressed by transport or lambing.

Last night I suffered the ultimate humiliation. The Gaffer lets me out onto the lawn just before he goes to bed, the phone went – he was nattering on there for ages and the twit forgot to let me back into the house. I ended up spending the whole night outside. Luckily it was dry and fairly mild and there were loads of sheds I could sleep in.

Sooty, the farm cat, was absolutely delighted of course, as between us we gave the few resident rodents a sleepless night. We didn't actually catch any but we certainly worked out their motorway network so we have a better idea where to patrol from now on.

A great big dog fox actually had the audacity to walk right across the farm yard and set off the security lights not more than 20 yards from where I was sleeping. I soon chased that varmint off the premises but he could run much faster than me.

When the old feller came out in the morning he seemed to think it highly amusing that I had spent the whole night outdoors. It wasn't too bad as a one off but I wouldn't want to make a habit of it.

It's Saturday 17th March, 2001 and we have a phone call today from MAFF telling us that our neighbour with a suspected case of Foot and Mouth now has the all clear. This means that our Form D notice has been withdrawn. Even though our neighbour had to 'pull the plug' on his milk all week he received no compensation whatsoever. If you are going to dump several hundred quids worth of milk a day without compensation you are less likely to report a suspected case anyway.

A similar situation occurred at the start of the BSE epidemic when no compensation was being paid and farmers were not reporting suspected cases.

At the moment we are getting many cases of cows with 'slurry heel' (digital dermatitis). This causes extreme lameness within a very short time. We've got a few in-calf heifers running with the dairy cows and this always triggers it off. It is really easy to treat. When any lame cow comes into the parlour the affected foot is washed off with the udder washer, she is then milked and by the end of milking, when the foot is dry, Terramycin Spray is sprayed over the affected area. The hair grows much longer alongside the affected area. Two or three spray treatments are usually sufficient.

More cases are present if the slurry is loose from low dry matter silage, feeding too much low dry matter feed – in our case stock feed potatoes, cows not having a sufficient area of concrete and constantly standing in a few inches of slurry.

One of the biggest contributory factors seems to be temperature. When the weather gets colder, the number of new cases seems to disappear. Towards the end of the Winter there are more cases caused not only by the build-up of infection, but also because of the rise in temperature.

Farming next door to a village means that several public footpaths cross our fields. Normally these footpaths are quite extensively used and the people who use them are very considerate and sympathetic to the requirements of the countryside.

However, now that all footpaths are closed to the public, it is noticeable how there are pheasants contemplating making their nests in hedgerows immediately alongside footpaths which would normally not occur. Perhaps this enforced holiday from the disturbances of walkers will give our wildlife population a much needed boost.

Neither the Gaffer or Gareth are interested in shooting and neither owns a shotgun, but during the Winter feed hoppers containing wheat are constantly replenished to maintain the pheasant and other wildlife numbers.

I have been having several 'sitting' sessions lately. The new telescopic loader we bought has enough space for me to sit on the right-hand side of the seat. However, there are two drawbacks. One is the wet weather which means that my feet are filthy and already the inside of the cab looks like a dog kennel. The other is that in an emergency stop, or going over rough ground, I keep falling off my perch.

The Gaffer has decided in his infinite wisdom to make a box for me to sit in. An hour with a sheet of plywood, a chainsaw and some self tapping screws and a folded-up seed potato sack on the floor means I now have my own compartment. Most of the time I spend sitting and observing but it is also big enough for me to lie down if necessary. We made certain it is too short and too narrow for that dopey Jake (Sandra and Carl's Labrador) should he wish to take my place.

Now that the postman leaves the mail in a box by the farmyard gate, I am missing my daily tit-bits that he always gives me – I call him Bonio.

Once again at this time of year we are beginning to see bare brown patches appear in some of the grass fields. Some of these patches can cover a few acres and are caused by the feeding habits of leatherjackets. These are the larval stages of the crane fly, and are up to 3 cm in length, brown in colour with a very tough leathery outer skin. If you dig down into the soil you will see them feeding on the roots of the grass or indeed any vegetation. They can be controlled by sprays but at the moment the land is too wet to get on with any machines.

My assistant Pest Control Officer – that's Sooty the farm cat, must have been a steeplejack in a previous existence. Every day when the weather is favourable she gets up on the roof of the farm buildings. She gets up there and can hear the birds building their nest under the eaves and when they come out the pesky thing catches and kills them. I keep telling her that it is totally unnecessary and she has promised to try and break the habit. It would be far more sensible to devote her time to help me kill rats and mice.

You may be wondering how a lowly canine like myself can have developed my humanoid skills to such a high degree. It all really started about three years ago when I was still a teenager and Tracey and her cousin went backpacking around the world. We started writing to each other and it all developed from there.

I seem to have this thirst for knowledge and want to accumulate as much information as possible. At night if the light is not left on I make a hell of a row and now they are always left on. This is so that all the newspapers and farming publications that are stacked on the end of the sofa where I sleep can be read. I also stay in the milking parlour most milkings – with whoever is milking and listen to the latest news bulletins.

It is Monday 19th March and the whole country is becoming crippled by the Foot and Mouth crisis. So far there are 323 confirmed cases with no signs of new cases slowing down. MAFF has the potential to turn a crisis into a disaster. We regularly hear of up to five days between confirmation of a disease and eventual slaughter, then up to five days from slaughter to burning.

Why can't the vet who confirms the disease also assist in the immediate valuation and slaughter? There are plenty of out of work slaughter men who could be called in to help. There are also plenty of farm contractors with earth moving machines and spare labour because the farmers are afraid to allow them onto their farms. This is what happened in the 1967 outbreak, but now with all the bureaucracy and form filling, it is no longer possible.

In the worst affected areas of the country – Cumbria and Southern Scotland and Devon – the latest MAFF master plan is to kill any sheep or pigs within two miles of an outbreak irrespective of whether or not they are infected. It is hoped this will form a fire-break around the immediate areas of infection and help with eradication of this awful disease.

The army has now been called in to help with the disposal of carcasses in these worst affected areas. However, no national state of emergency has been declared as this would mean cancellation of the General Election on 3rd May. What is really needed is a can-do, kick-ass type of guy to oversee and organise the whole operation.

Another area that seems to be very badly neglected in the affected areas is vermin control. Vermin do not wipe their feet on disinfected mats before visiting another farm. In the 1967 outbreak, very rigorous vermin control was exercised within three miles of an outbreak – especially of rats and foxes.

The last four days at Faulty Farm have been eerily quiet as the Gaffer has been into hospital for an operation. Nothing life threatening but he seems to make a hell of a fuss of it. Neither Gareth nor the Missus has had time to take me anywhere and I have been bored out of my mind. For several days after he arrives home he just stays in the house being miserable. Fortunately the weather is wet so he is not tempted to go outside anyway.

Fifteen years ago, people spent 25 per cent of their income on food. Now this figure is down to just 10 per cent. Having new cars, two foreign holidays a year, designer clothes and all sorts of other luxuries are becoming common place. More money is also spent on keeping one's body looking good, whether by exercising or going to the gym and ever more so by cosmetic surgery. After one superb looking old dear went out of the shop the other day, the old feller said if she has another face lift and a tummy tuck she will nearly have to shave every day.

One compensation of having the Gaffer laid up is that he has stopped smoking that damned pipe in case he starts coughing and rips his stitches out. What seems to cause him the most grief is if he sneezes. If I can see he has a sneeze coming on, I am out of his way like a rocket.

The only people who seem to have any time for me at the moment are Tracey and Moose so I am spending extra time up at the shop helping with the building work. The roof is on, walls plastered, electrical wiring in place, pipes moved, door moved and today we are knocking a hole through into the shop itself, which means the hoover is going flat out to collect the dust.

One of the more interesting finds is an old *Western Mail* dated 14th September, 1984. 1984 was a drought year and on this date the Autumn floods had just started but they were nothing like as serious as the Autumn of 2000.

Petrol prices in South Wales rose by between 2p and 3p per gallon but these prices were not expected to stick. The rise was blamed on sterling's fall against the dollar. The price is now up to 182p per gallon.

The television programmes were - Wildlife on One, Emmerdale Farm, Give us a Clue, Des O'Connor Tonight, The Invisible Man, etc. so they haven't really changed that much.

The Agriculture Minister was Mr Michael Jopling. Milk Quotas had only been introduced in the April of this year. Britain's deputy Agriculture Minister at this time was John McGregor.

Monmouth Market report : Cattle light steers, max. 93p/kg. Medium max. 98p/kg. Heavy max. 100p/kg. Medium heifers max. 92p. Heavy max. 90p. Light lambs max. 141.3p/kg. Standard max. 144p/kg.

Sterling suffered its worst ever humiliation against the US Dollar tumbling to a new low of 1.2415. The UK Bank Base Rate was 12 per cent. The country was still in the grip of the Coalminers' Strike.

Every year I am expected to compete, in a number of dog shows and, in fact, I do rather enjoy it, as the person who trains me beforehand and who takes me to the show is Tracey. For several weeks she has me jumping through car tyres, running up ramps, under tarpaulin sheets and over water jumps. The show we are preparing for at the moment is held in the West Midlands -and I am in the working dog class - which in fact could be almost any breed.

The big day arrives, a final grooming and off we go, the Missus, Tracey and myself zooming up the motorway to another great day out. The show is split into three sections - obedience, appearance and obstacle course. I do find the Brummie accent a little difficult to understand and note a slight resentment to the only Taffy in the tournament.

The first section is the obedience test where I have to retrieve, sit, run and generally do everything that Tracey tells me to do. We end up winning this section by a narrow margin from a rather handsome Labrador with a strange name - I can't remember if it is supposed to be double o or Zero.

The second part of the competition is really on looks and personality. Here I am beaten into second place by this male model Zero. He is a handsome devil but by looking at his coat and general appearance I rather doubt if he has done a day's work in his life.

There are over 30 dogs in the class and it is now a dead heat between lover boy and myself with only the obstacle course to go to decide the winner.

To increase the excitement lover boy and myself run off against each other in the very last heat of the day. He is a cocky bugger and says that with his superior size and strength he will easily win. Tracey says to take no notice of his taunts but to just do my best. The Missus also gives me plenty of encouragement and says the Gaffer will be delighted if I win. I have decided to do my best going the one way and if necessary will have to introduce my contingency plan at the far end.

The flag comes down and I'm off with a five yard lead over lover boy, who was doing a bit of posing. Through the loop, under the tarpaulin, up the ramp and down the other side, over the waterjump and to the turn at the sandpit end where I am amazed to find that lover boy is deal level with me.

'Nice tight turn now', says Tracey, 'no Bennie not too wide', not realising that this is my contingency plan. When I am within a metre of Zero One I pick up a paw full of sand and throw it straight into his face, temporarily blinding him.

Away I go with my new found advantage and end up coming first by over 10 metres to a great roar of applause. But wait a minute, stewards come over to ask Tracey what happened to Zero at the far end. Quick as a flash she says he must have been stung by a wasp which allays their suspicions of foul play.

What happened next caught me completely off guard. Zero comes over and starts giving me a hell of a hiding and has to be pulled off by his irate owner, who was unaware of the sandpit incident. If there's one thing I can't stand it's a bad loser, can you?

Bringing us back up to date, the weather in this last week of March is still very wet but much milder. Potato grading continues on an almost daily basis. The prices are gradually increasing for top quality but a lessening of demand for below average samples. Increasing quantities of new potatoes are coming in from abroad.

There are now over 750 confirmed cases of Foot & Mouth with the rate increasing by up to 40 a day. The Army has been called in to help with the disposal of slaughtered stock but there is still a huge backlog. Slaughtered stock are now being buried in huge pits in preference to burning. This sometimes means these dead animals are transported long distances because in parts of the country where there are upland farms there may be 6 inches of soil and two miles of rock.

Animals within two miles of an outbreak are now being slaughtered even if not affected and the whole situation is changing daily.

Now that the clocks have changed and with lighter evenings, this is the time of year that the country house market really comes alive when people thinking of moving to the country often combine a break with house hunting. The worst hit areas are those with reported Foot & Mouth cases. Even if one was allowed to view this type of property, they couldn't get a sale as no completion date could be set if the sellers kept any livestock that could carry the disease.

Those who suggest we stop eating meat so animals don't have to suffer in the future don't realise that if everyone stopped eating meat, 45 million animals would be slaughtered immediately.

Sheep, pigs and cows are reared for their meat. If there were no market for the meat farmers would not be able to afford to keep them. The whole countryside would be empty of animals, indeed many breeds would become extinct.

Vast areas of the countryside are unsuitable for crops, these would become barren wastelands, rare breeds of plants would be lost as they get choked out by weeds. Hedges would become overgrown so driving through the lanes would be like driving through a tunnel. With the ditches not cleaned out by farmers, many roads would become impassable in wet weather.

Hundreds of thousands of jobs would be lost in the agricultural support industries. Many villages would become ghost communities as people left through lack of work. Tourism would suffer because most of those who come to these shores do so to see the beautiful countryside that livestock farming has made.

This is reality. Don't kid yourself that the animals would still be running around. In my own case, if I did not have sheep to round up and cows to move twice a day for milking, life would hardly be worth living.

In the last few days special livestock movement licences are being issued on welfare grounds to allow stock to be moved to more suitable conditions. One example of this is tack sheep being moved back to the upland farm of origin ready for lambing. However, if there is a risk of spreading the disease movement licences are not issued, but in some cases the stock are slaughtered for welfare reasons and the carcasses burned or buried.

The disease seems to be particularly endemic in sheep but large numbers of cattle are also being slaughtered. It is estimated at present that 1.5 per cent of the UK dairy herd has been slaughtered which, with the current low numbers of milking cows, means we are unlikely to fill our milk quota again next year (2001-2002).

What has gone so horribly wrong with this whole Foot & Mouth saga?

The first thing the Government did was to ban all exports. This increased sheep journeys as the sheep were returned to farms from markets where they had mixed with other livestock. The first action should have been to ban livestock movements, but the Government failed to do that for four crucial days.

Let's be absolutely clear. Farmers are not to blame. Auction markets are not to blame. Sheep dealers are not to blame. The blame for this disaster lies with some grubby smuggler whose ignorance of or contempt for Britain has brought livestock farming and many other rural businesses to their knees.

It has come in because Britain is a soft touch for smugglers. Almost anyone can bring in pretty well anything they like into this country.

Now the Army has been brought in there are clear signs that the disposal problem is at last being tackled. It also implies, as does the announcement on vaccination, that all the Government's efforts so far have been too little and too late. Before the Government blames farmers it should look at itself and its own lack of effective action in the face of disaster.

Today is 31st March and we have a telephone call from MAFF informing us that we are under a Form D restriction because a farm one mile away has gone down with Foot and Mouth disease. This case is at least 10 miles from the nearest outbreak and is a cause for considerable concern as the people who have gone down have been taking all the precautions necessary.

April

Today is 1st April and is Tracey's birthday, and is also April Fool's Day so people are playing little pranks on each other.

Another case of Foot and Mouth disease was confirmed next door to the original one on the other side of the village. The case that was confirmed yesterday morning had all the stock (pigs, sheep and cattle) valued and slaughtered by this evening which was a fairly mammoth task.

Our Farming Unions have appealed to the Government to tighten controls to stop illegal meat imports, which is the most likely cause of the present epidemic. Sniffer dogs, as used in Foot and Mouth free countries such as New Zealand, and clear signs warning travellers of the dangers of bringing in foodstuffs, should also be imposed.

It is annoying that Foot and Mouth was recorded in Brazil and Uruguay in January, and Argentina and South Africa in February. The UK accepts regular deliveries of meat from each of these countries as well as from Zimbabwe, Namibia and Swaziland that have each confirmed regular recent outbreaks. None of these countries farms intensively. All practice sustainable and non-intensive agriculture so no way can it be blamed on intensive agriculture.

The results of the December livestock survey announced last week reveal a decline in the number of livestock in all categories across the UK. The number of suckler cows is down by 6 per cent, dairy cow numbers by 6.5 per cent and breeding ewe numbers were down by 7 per cent. These figures show the serious decline in profitability of all farming sectors.

It's 2nd April and we have a visit from the Army Logistics Team who are involved with our local cases of Foot and Mouth Disease, as we are within the two mile zone. They want to know our livestock numbers and farm boundaries so we are now wondering if our livestock will be killed. It is all very worrying and seems to be made worse because farmers are isolating themselves on their holdings and seldom see their neighbours for fear of spreading the disease.

We notice on our Form D restrictions that poultry carcasses (i.e. Christmas turkeys) could still be sold if the Ministry of Agriculture were to grant you a special licence. However, the thought of several thousand turkeys being collected and delivered from the farm would be a potential disaster waiting to happen. No AI by inseminators is allowed so the calving index of one's herd will be affected.

We have to inform our Milk Purchaser of our situation and obtain a relevant licence. Milk can contain the Foot and Mouth virus for three days before the cows show recognisable signs of the disease.

Some of the livestock being killed as at risk because of being in close proximity to an outbreak are not being burnt but are being buried, at specific burial grounds often over 100 miles from the farm of origin and transported by road in sealed lorries.

One of these burial sites is on the Epynt Mountain just above Sennybridge in Powys. This up to now is a non-infected area and quite understandably the local farmers are very concerned and are at the site protesting. Just look at the drainage pattern from Mynydd Epynt into the River Usk. If there is a Foot and Mouth outbreak near Brecon in the next couple of months, how will MAFF and the Ministry of Defence (MOD) justify what they have done?

Today is 4th April and the number of Foot and Mouth outbreaks has reached 1,000 cases with over 1 million livestock already shot or due to be. Even though the Army are helping out, because of the sheer size of the operation there is still a delay of sometimes up to a week between slaughter and disposal of the bodies. At present, there is a backlog of up to 300,000 animals slaughtered but awaiting disposal.

From our farmyard, we can see the smoke from the burning of the affected animals just one mile away. The wind changed direction today, so the smoke is blowing directly over us. Let's hope that no affected spores are going up in that smoke. The only smell that is really recognisable is the creosote from the railway sleepers, and the faint smell of coal.

The local Council Elections and the next General Election, which were scheduled for 3rd May, have now been postponed to 7th June because of the current crisis.

The Royal Show at Stoneleigh in the first week of July has been cancelled for this year. The old feller really enjoys the Royal but it was a necessary precaution in the light of current events.

One of the biggest casualties of this awful disease is the tourist industry. Our Government is trying to spread the message that the countryside is still open for business, but very few of the general public agree. Almost one-third of those who planned a holiday in the countryside over the coming Easter weekend have cancelled. They fear spreading the virus or taking it home and are confused over which areas and attractions are open. More than 90 per cent of footpaths and tracks are to remain closed over the holidays because councils are refusing to lift orders banning walkers from rights of way.

Here at Faulty Farm we are in a situation of being accused of spreading the disease. Here we are under a Form D notice but we have Jim and Adam and some dry sheep two miles down the road, and five miles away we have another farm with masses of farm buildings, where we store potatoes, grain and straw. We also keep our beef cattle and dairy replacements and some sheep there. Every day we have to go and check and feed these stock so we are potential carriers of the disease, even though we are always disinfecting and cleaning the vehicles. However, there is no way we could ask anyone else to do this job for us, as they would risk getting infected themselves.

The cull ewes that we are lambing at the away farm are now lambing thick and fast. We gave up the idea of lambing them outside and have brought them into the buildings to lamb. This means the idea of separation to keep our Pedigree flock free of Maeda Visna Disease could probably cost us our disease free status.

Tesco have just announced profits of over £1bn. This equates to a profit per day of £2.7 million. Part of this is due to a rise in food prices, but really it is the fact that the major supermarkets are profiteering.

These guys have it all their own way. They sell goods at below cost price to fend off local, small shops. This is gross profiteering and people need protection. They are exploiting farmers and consumers.

I really do not know what is going to bring British farmers to their knees – Foot and Mouth or MAFF. MAFF seem to change their rules daily and it is impossible to find out what these rules are. Some people are saying there should not be a public enquiry into the disease, as it will only make it worse for the farmers as they will get the brunt of the blame. It is the Government and MAFF who are entirely to blame – farmers over the years have had to abide by all their rules.

If we make a mistake in filling in their forms, we can lose a lot of money. If MAFF make a mistake, then as far as they are concerned it doesn't matter. It is time some of these people came out of their cosy offices, bought some Wellington Boots and spent time working on a farm.

I suppose when it is all over, the Government will admit some mistakes and say they will learn from them. Even if MAFF is accused of mismanagement, nobody will lose their jobs.

We really are hearing of some horror stories directly connected with outbreaks. Stock dead on farms for over a week if slaughtered because of being a dangerous contact. Trenches needing to be dug to stop blood and animal fluids from 5,000 dead sheep flowing onto a road. These culled sheep should not have been placed so close to the road, near the town of Tewkesbury.

A case near Gloucester where two sheep carcasses fell off a lorry taking them to a landfill site. MAFF tell the drivers not to bother to sheet the loads unless an animal is likely to fall off. The road was disinfected before traffic was allowed back on. I hope the driver of the lorry concerned has been put on other duties.

Defence and health officials are strongly denying a report that a test-tube containing the Foot and Mouth virus was stolen from the Porton Down defence research centre on Salisbury Plain two months before the start of the outbreak. It was reported missing following a routine audit.

It is even claimed the disease could have been an act of deliberate sabotage by a rogue MAFF worker and a protest group. Seems highly unlikely, but makes good reading in a Sunday newspaper.

Tony Blair made a huge gaffe this week by visiting affected areas of the country and declaring that it is still safe to visit, while wearing yellow waterproof trousers and jacket. He looked more as if he had just visited a damaged nuclear power station and must really have persuaded more people than ever to book foreign holidays.

Today is Sunday 9th April and we have another confirmed case two miles from here. This case is about two miles from the initial two cases a week ago. It concerns a fairly small number of sheep, but as yet there does not appear to be any obvious signs of how it could have spread, except for on the wind.

The slaughtered stocks from the initial two outbreaks were both burned on the same fire and six days later that fire is still smouldering.

The Foot and Mouth epidemic is threatening to engulf the whole of Britain after the virus spread to a previously unaffected part of the East Coast yesterday. This was to a farm in North Yorkshire, which was 40 miles from the nearest case, the virus's biggest jump so far. It comes a day after the virus made its previous biggest jump – 30 miles to the Scottish Borders.

Here in South Wales, we have another jump of 25 miles to Caerphilly near Cardiff. The person whose farm is affected has some land only about three miles from here, so it is possible that may be the contact, but as far as I am aware he has no sheep here.

Agriculture Minister Nick Brown has evoked farmers' fury by claiming that widespread illegal livestock movements could be responsible for the continued spread of Foot and Mouth disease. He said it is highly unlikely to be wind borne, but to be spread by movements of vehicles, people or livestock.

Our neighbouring county of Gloucestershire is becoming a real concern as cases rise over 70 with up to 11 confirmed in one day.

Independent vets in the County are claiming there are more cases in dairy cows if they are being fed maize silage rather than grass silage. They are claiming that the starlings, which can be a real problem with dry maize silage, are contributing to the spread of the disease. Here at Faulty Farm we have seen hardly any starlings at all this Winter.

We have been under Form D restrictions here at home for 10 days, and now with the new outbreak just down the Valley, the land where Jim and Adam and the dry sheep have been wintered has also come under a D Notice. The rules are changing almost daily, but at the moment we cannot move them for 14 days after a Notice has been served, and then only under Licence to D Notice land.

The land where these sheep are is due to be planted to Spring barley, but as of today (12th April) there is still no sign of the weather improving to allow ploughing to commence.

An articulated lorry has just gone up our road alongside the farm loaded with animals taken out as dangerous contacts. About 250 cattle and 1,200 sheep are involved. This week the haulage lorries are starting to take away the carcasses on the same day as shooting occurs, which is a vast improvement on only four or five days ago.

The number of confirmed cases now stands at just over 1,200, with claims that the number of new cases is levelling out.

It is now three weeks since the old feller had his stay in hospital and, even though he is still b..... miserable, he is not quite so unbearable as he was. He now wears a support around his ribs to ease the situation, which means he is back to driving too fast but has not yet started milking or throwing around potato sacks.

Potato grading and sales are continuing at a good rate, and we are now down to only about six weeks' supply still on the farm.

This coming weekend is Easter where the tourist trade should be starting in earnest, but the present restrictions mean people are not venturing into the countryside, and all the hotels, coffee shops, gift shops and other tourism related industries are really suffering. There is even talk of an extra Bank Holiday in the autumn for some of these rural businesses to help recoup some of their losses.

The tourism industry in the UK generates six times as much revenue as agriculture and they are really suffering at the moment. Local councils are talking of reducing business rates in rural areas, but nothing concrete has yet been decided.

Wales' very own Royal Welsh Show at Builth Wells has been cancelled today because of the current crisis. This show is certainly the shop window for Welsh farming and will be greatly missed.

The Foot and Mouth crisis has now been with us for two months and you just cannot believe the impact it is having on everyone and almost everything connected with the countryside.

There are far more birds nesting alongside now unused public footpaths, but this is probably the only plus side. Because no hunting takes place, we are more likely to see foxes, which do far more damage than most people realize, especially to newborn lambs. Everyone associated with tourism is suffering extreme hardship as visitor numbers have all but disappeared.

Farmers are under extreme financial and emotional pressure. Beef, sheep and pig farmers are having very little, if any, income due to closure of markets. Dairy farmers still have a milk cheque, but with milk at only 18p per litre, they are losing money on every litre produced.

One farmer in the county went onto a farm where cattle and sheep had been destroyed as dangerous contacts, and threatened the farmer and lorry drivers with being shot if they drove the loads of carcasses by his farm. The army personnel informed the police who later went and told him to grow up. Two days later this same guy was hauling slurry along a main road to spread on a neighbour's field and was going by two lots of other people's stock. He was not only forgetting to clean and disinfect his spreader (he was under Form D restrictions) but was leaving an awful mess on the road. It really does take all sorts!

There is talk at the moment of an early retirement scheme for farmers to vacate their holding and also for additional support for new entrants to the industry. This is to compensate for the lack of young people taking up farming as a career. All it really needs is for farming to become more profitable and there would be plenty more youngsters just dying to join the industry.

We have not heard a squeak out of the anti-fox hunting or animal rights groups who seem to have endless time on their hands to enjoy disrupting country sports.

It would be interesting to know how many of these people are helping in the front line of the crisis. There has not been any coverage of them disrupting any of the desperate cruelty incurred by often faulty methods of containing the disease. Many skilled hunt staff volunteered help and, much to the Government's distaste, are involved in helping to speed the necessary disposals humanely.

A farmer had his entire flock of sheep slaughtered by MAFF officials who misread a map reference; seems typical of the ramshackle handling of this sorry saga. The farm where the slaughter should have taken place was 100 miles away.

First the tentative, mustn't frighten the voters moves, which precipitated a full blown crisis. Then panic slaughter before preparing proper burial pits. Vaccination not being the answer until, suddenly, it becomes the answer.

God help this country if it ever faces a threat worse than Foot and Mouth disease.

It's now the middle of April and the weather is starting to dry up and we have two muck spreaders going for several days, trying to catch up with the backlog of work. The Gaffer is back tractor driving (too fast over rough fields) and he is also back milking. In fact he is nearly back to his old self – i.e. damn miserable. I did miss the old so-and-so being around as he always takes me with him.

Have just had a day lifting potatoes that we failed to get out last Autumn. About half of them had rotted completely due to the frost and wet weather, but what we got out was surprisingly good. We should have waited another few days for the ground to dry more and then we would have ended up with less soil in the trailers.

The number of cases of Foot and Mouth has now dropped to about 15 per day, which is about one-third of three weeks ago. The Government look poised to ease Foot and Mouth restrictions in certain counties. Under the new measures, healthy animals will be allowed to be sent for slaughter to local abattoirs, which will improve meat supplies to the shops and provide a life line for hard-hit farmers.

I feel the Army must be congratulated for their magnificent efforts in coordinating the disposal of slaughtered stock. More than 70,000 animals have been disposed of in our neighbouring county of Gloucestershire alone, with far more in the worst affected areas of Devon and Cumbria. Affected farmers where the Army has been involved have nothing but praise for their efficiency and understanding.

There is much debate at the moment about vaccination to help control the disease. One of the problems would be that we cannot export stock. One of the main problems is the disease being carried into and spread by the wildlife.

The Government was yesterday accused of recruiting unskilled workers to spearhead a massive vaccination programme. These workers are being sought through job centres and would be trained by using oranges to practise their vaccination skills. The Ministry are ignoring offers of help from over 50 vets and slaughtermen with previous experience of animal husbandry.

The Food and Drink Federation dealt the plans another blow by saying it did not want meat or milk from inoculated animals to enter the food chain. At the moment they are only talking about vaccinating cattle in which case the virus would just get passed back and forth by sheep, which come into contact with vaccinated cattle.

People now want the best food they can get plus the wildflowers as well. This is not a disaster for agriculture. It is a rock solid assurance that there are good times ahead for those farmers with the initiative to get into the market place and explain the facts about the countryside and how it works.

We are going to have to form local or county co-operatives as already happens on the Continent. These will then source local food, slaughtered and processed locally and sold through the co-operatives own supermarkets.

There is also a growing market for Internet selling and home deliveries. We people who grow and produce the food have to try and cut out the middle men who make far greater profits than we do with far less risks involved.

Today is 20th April and I saw the first swallow arrive at Faulty Farm. It spent most of the day perched on an overhead cable in the hope that its mates would soon arrive. This is about the normal date for the first to arrive but it will be towards the end of the month until the majority are here.

Today we finally start ploughing which must be one of our latest starts ever. We have Spring barley to plant – some for combining and some to be undersown with grass and cut as whole crop silage. There is no maize to be planted but a fairly large acreage of potatoes, so it will be towards the end of May before we finish planting assuming we have no wet weather from here on.

The O Strain of the Foot and Mouth virus, which is the virus we are dealing with at the moment, was originally diagnosed in Mongolia. It then spread to China and on to India, and subsequently jumped continents to South Africa. It then appeared in Turkey and Greece and spread all across Russia. It has now ended up here, in the Netherlands and in France.

When you consider the amount of illegal bushmeat coming in, together with the amount of meat being imported legally from countries suffering from Foot and Mouth, it is hardly surprising that we end up with the problem. Even Sir John Krebs, chairman of the Food Standards Agency, has admitted there are adequate requirements set in place to monitor imports of meat, these requirements appear to be poorly enforced.

Hundreds of farmers may be forced to quit because of mounting debts. Many farmers whose animals have been slaughtered will have to hand over their compensation cheques simply to clear their overdrafts. The bank having got out will be more reluctant to extend themselves to that level again. Many farmers will be looking at their compensation money as redundancy payments and will decide to opt out.

The farmers who have not directly been affected will have seen a negative cash flow and these people, especially the tenants, will be very badly hit.

The North Wales island of Anglesey was very badly affected by the disease in the early stages of the epidemic, resulting in almost 50,000 animals being slaughtered in a very determined effort to wipe out Foot and Mouth in the island.

Now we have a situation where seven smallholders (with outside incomes to supplement their lifestyles) refuse to let MAFF slaughter their pet livestock and so put the health status of the entire island at risk. This is an absolutely disgraceful act of selfishness, and unbelievably the Welsh Assembly has caved in to their wishes.

Here in Wales we have the MAFF and the Welsh Assembly jointly running the show, and as happens all too often, the Welsh Assembly show how completely spineless they are.

An end to the disposal of carcasses at Epynt Mountain near Sennybridge has just been announced. The pyres will continue until all the remaining carcasses in the pit have been burned, but there are no plans to take more animals to the site.

A slaughterman from Cumbria is believed to have contracted Foot and Mouth disease – the first human to fall victim to the virus during the current crisis. If the tests prove positive, he will become only the second person in the UK to have contracted the disease since an outbreak in the 1960s. His condition is 'giving no cause for concern'. Apparently the symptoms soon disappear and the disease is not spread by humans.

Agriculture Minister Nick Brown admitted today that fears that shoppers would shun products from inoculated cattle had forced him to shelve plans for a vaccination programme. When asked if farmers had a veto over vaccination, he replied – 'no, consumers do.' If anyone has a veto it's public opinion.

It's not so much the amount of change, which British Agriculture has undergone in the last five years that is so bewildering as the speed at which it has taken place. An industry that was used to things evolving at a gentle, almost sedate pace has seen its members running ever faster to keep up on a treadmill that has gone out of control.

We have now applied fertilizer to all the grazing, mowing fields and the Winter cereals. Of the fields of Winter wheat and Triticale that we planted in the middle of January, the wheat is all OK to leave even if a little thin in places. However, the Triticale is rather poor and two fields will be replanted. The seed seemed to take about two weeks longer to emerge than the wheat and this delay, coinciding with severe flooding, caused its failure.

The 22nd April and the number of cases of Foot and Mouth are now into single figures each day. However, a complete change in the weather – cold, heavy rain all day with an awful forecast for the next week so we are back to potato grading which is good for the cash flow.

The dairy cows are now out to grass even though it is too cold for much to grow. They are out by day and have the choice to stay in or out at night, but they all go out. This cold wet weather caused the first case of Hypomagnesaemia of the season. This was a cow that had been calved for three months and caused by a deficiency of magnesium, change of diet, stress, cold wet weather, etc. A bottle of magnesium sulphate injected under the skin had her back on her feet grazing within an hour. I always prefer if they lie quietly for an hour after being injected or they can end up doing the splits or worse still fall on top of me, as they are staggering around.

Today is 23rd April and we have a Movement Licence to move Jim, Adam and the ewe lambs back home as it is two weeks since the second outbreak in our area. They were on someone else's land which was a Form D as is ours here at the farm. We could not have moved them to our off-lying land as that is in a 'cleaner' area. We had to thoroughly clean and disinfect the cattle trailer and a MAFF Vet had to come and inspect the sheep for any symptoms of Disease.

These sheep are now in the field right next to the house so Jim and I had a long chat today. He still knows nothing about the Foot and Mouth implications and is just hopping mad that the Gaffer left them away from home and short of grass for no apparent reason. He is adamant that he is going to give the old boy a series of butts from behind to get his own back. I am seriously trying to talk him out of this attitude problem of his, but if he persists I must make certain I go into the field with the Gaffer to protect him. The old man is only just recovering from an operation so we don't want him with a broken leg as well with such a backlog of work to catch up with.

The Government has admitted that the huge pyres of burning livestock could be harmful to the health of people living nearby, because of the acrid cloud of smoke. Asthma sufferers in particular are being affected. It has also been accepted that micro organisms from carcasses could enter local water supplies.

After the 1967 outbreak many fish stocks became depleted in rivers close to sites where animals had been buried, burned or where high levels of disinfectants had been used. The most likely cause was the disinfectants killing off the lower plant and animal life in the water courses with the result that there was less plant and animal food for the fish to live off.

One of the Missus's cousins was on the phone today, who farms 25 miles away, to say they have just gone down with Foot and Mouth disease and all the sheep and cattle are to be slaughtered.

It's now 25th April and the swallows have really arrived in force. The buildings are a hive of activity as they are already searching for nesting sites.

Now that the cows are out both day and night, I have to help get them in for milking but my problem is that I am very easily distracted – especially in the mornings with all the fresh wildlife smells and I forget about the cows and go rummaging through the hedgerows. Needless to say, this does not improve my popularity with a certain person. However, it is much more pleasant being out in the fields for the cows than living in cubicles and walking on concrete for six months of the year.

Some of the cows that only a few weeks ago were lame and suffering from arthritis are suddenly much better. Several times a year we have a professional foot trimmer come in to sort their feet out but with the current restrictions, this is not possible. Gareth and his old man have a go at the worst ones, but without a proper foot-trimming crush, it is rather difficult.

We've got a rather ancient JCB on the farm and at the moment are trying to repair broken and collapsed drains and cleaning out ditches. I spent the first hour or so checking out any wildlife in the hedgerows and the rest of the day sat in the cab of the machine. I really wish they would repair the exhaust pipe to save so much smoke coming in. At this time of the year I take great care not to disturb any nesting birds off their eggs.

The Pick-Your-Own field is suddenly bursting into life with this year's crops. Blackcurrants, strawberries and raspberries have all had their pre-emergence spray programmes that should ensure a reasonably weed free growing and harvesting season. Even though we use sprays, we are very selective and do not practice Insurance spraying but go in only when it is deemed absolutely necessary.

There is much debate at the moment over trials of Genetically Modified (GM) crops being grown in the UK. The public certainly are not in favour nor are the majority of farmers – especially the organic farmers who fear cross-pollination and contamination of their own crops.

With all the food scare stories at the moment, it would appear more sensible to let the dust settle for a few years before going ahead, but some big plant breeders and pharmaceutical companies stand to make huge profits, and because they make large contributions to Labour Party funds, they have the full backing of our Government.

A month ago the Government was talking of reducing business rates for rural businesses and shops or giving them a rates holiday. What has happened is that no rates are due this March or April, but in March and April of next year they have to pay twice as much. Gareth is having a good moan about it – the boy is unfortunately starting to pick up some of his old man's habits.

Phoenix the Charolais heifer calf that has arisen from the Ashes has caught everyone's attention at present. Her mother and loads of other cows were slaughtered as dangerous contacts but she was trapped underneath the bodies for several days.

The public seemed perfectly prepared to accept the slaughter of over two million animals – many of them very young, as a price worth paying to combat the disease.

For a Government obsessed with spin and presentation the impending death of Phoenix the calf was the ultimate nightmare. As the story grew and public support for the calf increased, Downing Street was faced with a PR nightmare. Suddenly out of the blue Phoenix would be allowed to live as a result of changes to the slaughter policy. From now on there would be no contiguous cull (mass slaughter of all stock within two miles of an outbreak). Phoenix left the Government in a no-win situation. She has been seen as a symbol of hope for the farming industry and we all wish her well.

Organic milk supply exceeds demand! An organic dairy marketing co-operative is having to sell some of its milk into the conventional milk pool because the UK organic market has become over supplied. In fact, only 70 per cent of their total milk output will be sold through the premium organic market. The remaining 30 per cent of output will be sold at realisation value. This must be a bitter blow to anyone newly converted to organic who needs a premium price for their milk to compensate for the lower production.

The Government keeps saying it wants more and more farms to convert to organic farming and in fact most farmers would convert if they could afford to, but realise that in not many years' time the organic premiums that are being paid at present will almost disappear.

It is claimed that 70 per cent of all organic food is imported but they forget to say what percentage of this is exotic fruits and vegetables that cannot be grown in our climate.

Farmers whose livestock has been trapped by the Foot and Mouth restrictions were dealt another devastating blow yesterday. The Agriculture Ministry said if farmers can no longer afford to feed the animals, they would just have to give them away. Lack of money for feed will be classed as a welfare issue and the Government will remove and destroy the animals free of charge but the farmers will be paid nothing for them.

This edict comes hard on the heels of a decision to slash compensation for slaughtered stock. Payments are coming down by about 40 per cent. It looks like another example of how this Government is using the crisis to clear farmers off the land.

Three suspected cases of Foot and Mouth Disease in humans has just been confirmed negative which is a huge relief.

At the moment about 20 per cent of farmers have 80 per cent of total Subsidy Payments. Any future Farm Subsidies look most likely to support Income rather than Output.

Gareth is back ploughing but only some fields are dry enough and the Gaffer and I are spraying when it is not too wet or too windy. We have a lightweight self-propelled sprayer which is an absolute joy to ride in and a fully enclosed cab so that I get absolutely no draught coming in at all. However, in just one day the stupid twit managed to get it stuck not once but twice. The first time we got out ourselves after a lot of shouting and cussing, but the second time we were really bogged in to the axles and had to be towed out. I tried to tell him where the wet patches are but he took no notice at all, which is just typical.

We have now finished building the new extension to the shop in the village and the new shelving has eventually arrived, so now we have many more lines on display for sale.

One casualty of the Foot and Mouth crisis is the humble honey bee. Not only do they have the problem of the Veroa Mite but now Foot and Mouth. Many of the hives are on farmers' land and the owners cannot get to them to feed and check their well being. This is the start of the most critical stage of their year with the need for pollination of plants. I really do wonder how many fruit and veg. would be on our supermarket shelves if it were not for the efforts of pollinating insects and birds.

Only days after the Anglesey 'Seven' won a reprieve to save their livestock from slaughter, one of the holdings has had their stock slaughtered because of possible Foot and Mouth.

I'm told I have bad breath. The trouble is a loose decaying tooth caused by an old war wound. A few years ago I was rabbiting, chased this rabbit into a large earth and was confronted by this great big badger. When I am in hunting mode unfortunately I have no reverse gear and made the mistake of having a go at him. Anyway the result of this scrap, in marks out of 10, was 10 to him and 0 to me.

The Gaffer says unless something is done with this problem of mine he will not take me with him in the vehicle any more, so an operation to remove the tooth it must be.

Tracey takes me to Colditz Veterinary Hospital and hands me over to, yes you've guessed it, big Ally who is suitably dressed for the occasion. I can't decide if he is a wannabe David Gower or Muhammed Ali. He's wearing a cricketer's box and also boxing gloves with a syringe of anaesthetic and what seems to be a knitting needle protruding from it.

I immediately revert to my coward's mode and look for ways to escape. On the operating table I see all sorts of operating instruments, including pliers. I am driven entirely by fear and end up escaping onto the top cupboard. One of the nurses is showing a large amount of cleavage which normally would have me spellbound but not today.

Muhammed Ally grabs me from behind and quick as a flash sticks his huge needle in my backside and injects me with the anaesthetic. It takes some time to go under during which time the Alligator is taunting me and feeling pretty smug with himself, and I'm thinking Maltesers, Maltesers; they melt in your mouth, not in your hand, so be careful buddy boy. He then puts me to sit in this dentist's chair and the last thing I remember doing is crossing my legs before dozing off.

As I'm coming round after the operation to remove my tooth I am aware of this pain in my mouth and by listening to their conversation it is obvious they have as great a mistrust in me as I have in them.

I pretend to be still out of it as I see Big Ally removing his protective gear and I'm thinking step a little closer big feller and let's see if the swelling has gone down from last time.

Miss Cleavage is still hovering around but it's someone else I have in mind. Big Al is sat on the edge of the bed not realising I am coming around and has the audacity to break wind. I am hallucinating and believe I can see two big juicy steaks in place of his arse and sink my teeth in to the hilt.

His scream carries outside to where Tracey is waiting to pick me up. On entering the surgery and enquiring about the noise big Al says he was just arseing around. On leaving I noticed him searching for a Tetanus injection for himself. On a score out of 10 basis this time I would say 5 for me and 5 for the opposition.

You just won't believe it but now I have to clean my teeth every day to prevent any further decay. My own idea of cleaning my teeth would be to sink them into a fully grown rat, but no they have actually given us a machine to do it, in actual fact it's an electric toothbrush. Tracey says she will do it for me when she has time but to do it myself I will have to wedge it into an opening about a foot off the ground and work my mouth around the brush rather than the brush around my mouth.

Tuesday 1st May and still the weather has not settled and would you believe it, but we have done absolutely no planting of cereals or potatoes. The Gaffer says that there has been the very rare occasion when he has planted cuckoo barley (i.e. in the last 10 days of April after the cuckoo appears) but he has never ever planted in May.

We are on reasonably heavy land but with an impervious subsoil and in an area of 36-38 inches of annual rainfall. Today we had every intention of planting one field of barley, but the soil was far too wet. When it is compressed in your hand it stays the shape of a ball of plasticine rather than breaking up.

Gareth then goes ploughing and the Gaffer and I have a day spreading fertilizer. Some of the fields of Winter wheat have the worst ruts in them that we have ever seen due to the constant heavy rain. In fact if you had a two-wheel drive tractor and ended up with the front wheels in one of these ruts, you would be stuck. I normally like to sit on top of the toolbox alongside the old boy, but after falling off my perch a few times I end up sitting on the floor.

Normally on our off-lying farm we see several hares but so far this year we have not seen any, so we hope they are just hiding from us.

Officials now claim that up to 25 per cent of farms where livestock have been slaughtered were actually free of the disease. Farmers' leaders are calling for a public inquiry to investigate the issue, which has led to hundreds of people seeing their life's work wiped out for nothing.

Two weeks after the start of the outbreak Ministry Vets were told to slaughter all animals as soon as they suspected the disease to be present. The order came after complaints from farmers about the length of time it was taking to get results from blood tests, which were taking up to four days.

With the number of new cases now down to six or eight a day and the disease now apparently under control, MAFF has scaled back on its culling operations.

Four giant mobile incinerators in Gloucestershire have now cleared the backlog in that county and two are being sent to Devon and a third to a farm near Welshpool in Powys. Here 1,500 sheep were buried in a mass grave but torrential rain and rising underground water levels means that blood is rising to the surface. These sheep were buried five weeks ago and will now be dug out and incinerated on site. I hope the persons who sanctioned the initial burial operation spend a few days moving these rotting, stinking carcasses.

This really must be the most amazing time of the year for anyone associated with the countryside and nature. This morning I see a blackbird with a worm in her beak and tadpoles wriggling in a tiny pond at the side of the yard. The swallows are darting everywhere with bits of wool and materials to make their nests and some have even laid their eggs and are sitting patiently hatching them out.

Sooty, the farm cat, still practises her appalling feline habit of killing these harmless birds, in spite of my constant rebukes. The Missus gives her extra food and I have even offered to share mine, but it's not because she is hungry, it's just her natural instinct. She does assure me she is making a real effort to stop this unnecessary slaughter, but it is really difficult.

Jim, the senior stock ram, is still here in the field next to the house and his dislike of the Gaffer seems to increase each day. Gareth and the Missus are OK by him, but I really do worry for the safety of the old boy should he venture into the field without me.

We have just been completing our 2001 Census Form. These are now compulsory every 10 years, and would you believe it – there was no mention of whether or not any pets were kept at a household. I find this fairly typical of the high-handed way this Government runs the country and I am seriously thinking of writing to my MP.

The 2nd May and we are lifting potatoes. Trouble is they are last year's potatoes. About 50 per cent have rotted off with the frost, or wet weather and what are OK have shoots on them 3-4 inches long and so we end up with more soil in the trailers than potatoes. The ones that are good are of excellent quality so they are well worth getting out.

The field we are lifting from is alongside a river so I spend most of the day exploring. A lot of debris and trees are partly blocking the river after last year's floods so we should really get a winch to remove them some time.

At one end of the field are a family of mink so I steer clear of those varmints. A mink is a semi-aquatic flesh-eating mammal that has partially webbed feet, a soft thick coat and looks like a large weasel. The down side is that they are extremely nasty, and kill off all the fish and nesting birds along the water courses. I personally cannot think of anything useful about them, so the more that are destroyed the better.

The weather is still very cold and changeable with little land work being done except on the lighter soils, very little grass growth and it is only now that the first of the larger dairy herds are being turned out to graze.

In a dry early Spring if one can get the cows out by early April to lush grass, it is a real bonus, not only saving on silage and concentrate feeding, but getting a boost in milk production when the milk price is still reasonable. As a rule of thumb the milk yield should rise by about 10 per cent on turnout. More than 10 per cent and you were previously underfeeding, less than 10 per cent and you were overfeeding concentrates.

Had a tracked JCB 360 turn up today to clean out the slurry pit. It really concerns me to see this machine going round and round all day. I often wonder if the driver has to count how many times he turns anti-clockwise otherwise the top half would fall off.

The slurry from the cows is all pushed into a large above-ground pit every day in the Winter and once a year we clean it all out onto either potato or maize land and plough it in.

Several footpaths and rights of way have now been reopened in National Parks in readiness for this coming weekend Bank Holiday. Let us hope that the extra visitors will help to recoup some of the losses suffered by the hotels and guesthouses, etc.

I am dismayed by the selfish attitude of many farmers in recent months who think they are the only ones who have suffered. True there have been cases of extreme difficulty and hardship over recent months, but in the not too distant future we will be able to sell our stock (albeit at a reduced value) to generate some income.

If a hotel or guesthouse needs to have 50 per cent occupancy to cover its costs and they have nobody staying, it is a catastrophe. They may have been in this situation for three months or more with absolutely nothing to fall back on. We read of one country pub that took only £35 in one week, which would not even have paid for the electricity.

One of the more distressing aspects of Foot and Mouth is the way the epidemic and its ramifications have set farmer against farmer. Farmers have not always been known for singing from the same hymn sheet, but the petty jealousies over payments and whose stock went first under the welfare scheme (before the rates were cut) seem to have been magnified by stress.

Two farmers who were at the forefront of the outbreaks have been hospitalised with facial injuries after boasting too loudly down the pub about the size of their compensation payments.

Was it a risk to feed our servicemen on foreign meat imported from Brazil where Foot and Mouth is rife? The MOD says it 'believes' meat came from F&M-free Brazilian farms but they cannot prove it any more than it can be proved that this meat caused the outbreak.

The rot starts at the top. How can we ask British consumers to buy our home produce if the Government of the day won't. It is not good enough to pass the buck to the contracted caterers who are forced down the cheap route.

I heard an amusing joke today that was quite appropriate to a canine like myself. Tony Blair jogging through Hyde Park and comes across 'Dai the Hunt' carrying a cardboard box. 'What's in the box Dai?', asks Tony. 'Four young puppies Mr Blair, and I'm going to call them Blair Puppies'. 'That's really kind of you Dai', says Tony as he and his minder carry on jogging.

A week later Dai the Hunt and Tony meet up again. 'How are the Blair Puppies doing Dai?', enquires Mr Blair.

'I don't call them Blair Puppies any more, I now call them William Hague Puppies instead', says Dai.

'I'm very sorry to hear that', says Tony Blair, 'what's the reason?'

'They've opened their eyes', said Dai.

Spent part of today putting the potatoes that have just been lifted over the cleaner and it's as Gareth said – 'not worth bothering to lift them'. They did just cover the cost of lifting and grading but only because the price is good. At last year's prices it would have been a complete waste of time.

Most of our neighbours still have their tack sheep on their land. We are under a D Notice and, as most of these sheep come from farms that are only restricted, movement is not allowed, as you cannot move onto 'cleaner ground'. These sheep are now being kept on fields that should have been shut up for silage six weeks ago.

Everyone is panicking that if we have a drought, there won't be enough silage for the dairy herds next Winter. More people than ever look to be growing maize this year.

Heard the cuckoo today for the first time. This is probably the latest I have ever heard it, it's mostly around by 25th April at the latest. In recent years there has been a marked decline in the number of cuckoos in this area.

We've spoken to several people lately who have had their stock slaughtered because of Foot and Mouth. The ones who are going to continue farming are going to do so at a very much reduced stocking rate than previously. Then they were on a conveyor belt of rising prices and falling returns and couldn't get off and this has given them the respite they needed.

We have just managed to plant two fields of Spring barley. The seedbeds were not as good as they might have been and the late sowing date will make for an abysmal crop. If it was not for the Arable Area Payments it would not have been worthwhile. However, with the high cost of the seed and fuel, maybe they would have been as well left in 'set-aside', but we do need the grain and the straw for our own use.

The Red Cross have said today they would like to see basic First Aid incorporated in the Driving Test. What a good idea! I don't know about you, but personally I would not have a clue on what action to take. Although wait a minute! Just imagine having to give the Gaffer mouth-to-mouth resuscitation – ugh! It would be like kissing a badger – perhaps we'll give that one a miss!

The old boy said to me the other day he would like to be somebody's toyboy. I don't think there is any likelihood of that happening as he is unlikely to find a woman old enough!

We are now into the second week of May and the grass is really starting to grow. The beef and sheep farms have shut off and fertilized their fields for hay and silage and all of the larger dairy herds have been turned out.

Several dairy farms have been unable to turn out any earlier as they were short of grass due to grazing of tack sheep. They will insist on grazing these sheep on the fields closest to the building right up to the end of February. Twenty or 30 acres should always be shut off on 1st January to ensure turn out 10-14 days earlier (weather permitting). Half of the grass available in mid-April will have grown in January and February.

Prime Minister Tony Blair announced today that a General Election has been called for 7th June. Investment in, and reform of, public services would be at the heart of their election manifesto.

It's a fair bet you won't find a lot of space devoted to a grand strategy for the future of British Agriculture. For one thing, there are very few votes to be won in the countryside, which tends to have been painted a uniform blue for as long as people can remember. And for another, one of Labour's unspoken aims is on the point of being achieved: the ruthless whittling down of the farming workforce.

This will get rid of many of those who, but for subsidies, would have gone out of business years ago, thus ensuring that there is enough money available under the new environmentally friendly Common Agricultural Policy (CAP) to keep the rest comfortably afloat. What a huge regulatory burden and a reluctance to draw down agrimonetary compensation have failed to achieve has been finally completed by cheap imports and Foot and Mouth disease.

We'll have promises of a new deal for farmers and consumers and a move towards a healthier, safer food policy. It will conveniently ignore the fact that Labour hasn't a clue about the realities of food marketing – and that supermarkets, rather than the Government, are currently responsible for implementing any policy change. And when these guys don't fancy it, they don't do it: witness the beef labelling scheme, now so blatantly ignored by so many retailers nine months after it was meant to become compulsory.

We can expect to see a commitment to more organic output, together with a firmer commitment to GM food production – for a very good reason. It is those who head up the Food Standards Agency who believe that it is in all our interests, but are also convinced that once the consumer is able to benefit from GM foods, opposition to them will simply melt away.

We have managed to plant another three fields of barley and undersown them with grass seeds – these fields will be made into silage. We have decided this year not to plant any maize for silage simply because we have too much of a workload in the Spring and Autumn with the cereals and potatoes.

There is an above average chance of having a drought this summer with all the rainfall we have had in the previous 18 months, so not growing maize could be the wrong decision.

Potato planting is now continuing at a good pace with another two local guys driving tractors as well as the Gaffer and Gareth. In recent years we have seen a complete role reversal here on the farm. The old boy likes to see the potatoes planted in dead straight rows and he was the one who always pulled the beds up prior to destoning. Well would you believe it, but now he can't even drive straight so it is Gareth's job.

There are times when the old feller is about as much use as an ashtray on a Harley Davidson. I call him Percolator – because he is always on the boil.

The Gaffer does the potato planting with a really old tractor with not enough room in the cab for me to lie down, so I spend most of my time on one of the tractors that are bed tilling or destoning. On the front of the planter tractor there is a hopper containing fertilizer, which is placed into the rows alongside of and slightly deeper than the seed potatoes.

With the price of fuel so high we are using £80 worth per day on average, which is absolutely staggering, but there is no way we can do anything about it. I dread to think what it costs some of the really big boys and contractors. Last spring it was costing £50 per day for the same usage.

I am only hearing the cuckoo about twice a week now which is much less than a few years ago. Did you know that the first time you hear the cuckoo every year you are supposed to turn the money over in your pocket to give you good luck, and good health for the coming year! So don't forget!

We have MAFF here today to blood test the sheep. All sheep in an area covered by a D Notice have to be tested and clear of Foot and Mouth before the restriction can be lifted. This means that I do not have time to help with the potato planting but have to stay here to help with the sheep. About three-quarters of them have to have blood samples taken and who do you think was the first to be caught – Jim, and boy did it make him evil! I spent most of the morning trying to talk him out of inflicting serious injury to one of the vets.

The person in charge was a French/Canadian vet who I had difficulty understanding. There were also two MAFF vets and two Army guys doing the catching. The whole team were unbelievably obliging and very sympathetic to the plight of the farmers.

Sheep from mid-Wales that were exported to France in January, and were initially reported to be suffering from Foot and Mouth apparently were not affected at all. Sounds like some political goings on here.

We have also managed to plant one field of Spring beans. These will be combined in September and used for feeding to our own livestock, along with the cereals.

Some farmers who have had their stock slaughtered because of Foot and Mouth are having to wait up to 14 weeks for their compensation money from MAFF. By reading the newspapers, you get the impression that they are paid within days so it just shows how misleading some reports are.

Our strawberry plants are now all out in flower so the last thing we need at the moment is a late frost, which could decimate the yield. The PYO crops have made terrific growth in the last two weeks and seem to be reasonably weed and disease free at the moment. Peas, broad beans and runner beans have all been planted.

The first planted peas and broad beans are now well through the ground, and the peas seem to be attracting the entire rabbit population of the Parish so every spare moment I get I am on guard duty.

The Autumn-planted broad beans are now out in flower and should be ready for picking in about five or six weeks' time. We would be happier if there were more bees around to help with the pollination but a few warmer days should see the numbers increasing.

Gareth has just finished completing the IACS forms to be sent away to MAFF by the 15th May deadline. These are to include all acreages of combinable crops, set-aside, maize, forage acres, waste land, etc. and form the basis for any Arable Area Payments, and stocking densities to ascertain payments which will be payable in eight or nine months' time.

Of the first 1,579 so-called 'confirmed' cases of Foot and Mouth disease, 450 have been tested negative, so there is a lot of explaining to do by somebody! Anyone, that is, who is not one of the leading puppet masters of the EU which is still insisting on Britain's livestock numbers being cut by 15 per cent.

The problem is with the markets. The banks will get their mitts on the compensation money and clear the overdrafts before handing farmers back the change, which will leave a whole swathe of producers with too little cash to restock, and they will have to join the others who have already decided to leave the industry.

But with the export markets likely to be closed until at least the Winter, if not the Spring, there will still be massive overproduction of lamb and therefore massive overpayment of subsidies.

But fear not, come Christmas Foot and Mouth, the banks and the EU will have seen to it that Labour's leaner, meaner and more efficient farming industry is taking shape. And, of course, without a stain on the Government's hands.

It's remarkable what effect a few days' sunshine can have on the nation's morale. All of a sudden attention is turning to beaches and bikinis, and F&M has slipped down the agenda. Which is exactly how it was meant to be during the election campaign.

MAFF has at least managed to eradicate the disease as an issue, if not the disease itself. Cases are still being reported but the number of animals slaughtered is tailing off. When the rush was on to clear the decks for the Election, vets were ordered to shoot on suspicion and test afterwards, to maximise the killing. Once the Election was called the order was rescinded and they reverted to testing before slaughter so as few animals as possible would have to be killed in the shadow of the ballot box.

Hot weather, tractors working hard and air-conditioning! One of our bigger tractors that does the primary cultivations, bed tilling and destoning has had the air-conditioning stop working and boy what a disaster. It's OK for the Gaffer to say we cannot afford the couple of hours it would take to repair it, as he does not have to drive it at the moment. When it gets really hot you have to open the back window and then you get the dust coming in as well. Needless to say you don't catch me on that tractor at the moment. I make certain I get on the other one with the air-conditioning working.

There is now a lettuce shortage. What the supermarkets have done to British lettuce growers has now come back to haunt them, but a lot of other things will be soon as well, because farmers are getting out of everything. They cannot go on providing more and more for lower and lower prices. Supermarkets keep squeezing the prices down, but the costs keep going up. Sooner or later the wheel is going to come off in a big way.

Who do you believe in the Great Milk Debate? Bristol University scientists who say the White Stuff is the right stuff – or the animal rights group who portray milk as a pinta poison.

The first lot know what they are talking about and stick to the facts. The second are driven by motives which are based on emotions. And emotions lead to illogical, and in this case, farcical claims.

My deputy, Sooty, has been missing for the last 24 hours and when I tracked her down this morning, guess what – she is now the mother of three baby kittens so now my duties also include kitten-sitting. They say cats can't count but they can certainly multiply!

Biosecurity is the buzzword of the year especially since the outbreak of Foot and Mouth. Any farm is the source of food and shelter to many unwelcome visitors: flies, birds and rodents. Not only do these pests steal food but they transmit diseases as well.

Maize silage is attractive to many species, e.g. starlings, pheasants and badgers. Rabbits are another problem. Five rabbits eat as much grass as one sheep, so 30 or so rabbits can eat as much grass as one cow.

If all these freeloaders scrumping animal feed has got you fuming, then there is also the wastage of feed by broken bags and the awful mess created by soiling of this feed.

This year the oak is out in leaf before the ash. 'If the Oak is out before the Ash we'll only get a splash' (of rain that is). Personally I can't ever remember a year when the ash is out first but it makes for some interesting conversation.

You don't have to be mad to work here but it helps if you are. Potato planting progressing at a good pace, kit largely holding together, Gareth is head of the team, the two casual lads doing remarkably well, Missus supplying back-up, Tracey milking in the evenings and everyone hits the ground running with the exception of one person, who shall remain nameless, but you all know who I mean.

'The harder you work the luckier you get'. This saying is largely confined to sportspersons where the more training they do is rewarded in their achievements. This, however, applies to any profession as the harder you work the more money you make which means that you are perhaps luckier than most of your colleagues.

The Gaffer comes up with the most amazing ideas at times. His latest one is that he is going to learn to use the farm computer and even says he is going to go on a training course. (Perhaps he doesn't realise you have to pay for these courses.)

Gareth and the Missus are both computer literate but the chances of the old feller achieving this status is almost zero. It took us two years to teach him how to use a calculator; the first six months teaching him how to switch it on and off.

We are still grading spuds most mornings for an hour or so before we start planting but as we only have ambient storage, they are just starting to go soft. However, the income from just a few ton of spuds a day helps to keep the wolf from the door.

A recent study by HSBC Bank and the Agricultural Development & Advisory Service (ADAS) of milk production costs shows that the breakeven output for the average producer is 20.49 pence per litre. As the milk price average for the last year is less than this figure, it does not take a genius to work out that it is all for nothing. The average milk price for March was 17.88 pence per litre.

Gareth's shop in the village has not really been affected by the ravages of Foot and Mouth disease. The village shop can be one of the hubs of community life, a lifeline for those without cars, particularly the elderly. It provides not just food, drink and household items, but often a reason to go out and a vital source of human contact. He says he feels more like a social worker than a shopkeeper at times.

Rained off spud planting for half a day so spend some time calf-dehorning and other jobs that have been kept on hold for a wet day.

You cannot turn the clock back so they say, but that is precisely what the Government will be seeking to do once re-elected. The Foot and Mouth epidemic coming after BSE has been the ideal ammunition for those idealists who want to reform – or destroy – UK agriculture.

This body of opinion – of unknown size – says that the Common Agricultural Policy (CAP) needs radical changes. Farmers should not be paid subsidies to produce food that is not required, that is priced at 30 per cent above world prices.

Then there are the greenies – do away with chemicals, let the countryside go wild. To this has been added the false notion that Foot and Mouth was caused by what they call factory farming. Anyone with more than a dozen cattle in a shed or 50 sheep in a field is thought by some to be farming intensively.

But no one among those nice people, who don't have a clue as to what really happens on a farm, ever considers or talks about the necessity of the farmer to make a living.

The CAP was devised to provide sufficient food to feed the people of Europe by farmers assured a reasonable standard of living. If nothing else, Foot and Mouth has brought home to so many businesses in the rural areas how dependent they are on agriculture.

Those who want cheap food say that we can import, but for how long, and what about the issues concerning animal welfare, traceability, farm assurance, etc. that we have to abide by?

The instinctive reaction of people faced with falling returns is to produce more, as scale of production is the key to lower costs of production. When the milk price began a steep slide in the late 1990s, a number of dairy farmers reacted by borrowing more money to increase the size of their herds, housing facilities and quota.

This decision, mostly aided by farm business consultants, is the classic knee-jerk reaction of farmers encountering hard times. Far from helping it has pushed them even further into debt that must be serviced from a falling income.

A better response might have been to add value to the product by better marketing! Farmers have no right to a market. They just produce what they are good at producing and assume a market is available.

The average beef and sheep farmers either sell their produce on a deadweight basis, or take it to market where the auctioneers have assembled the buyers. The average milk producer gets his milk into the tank from where it is collected, processed, delivered and sold by somebody else.

Farmers keep moaning about the profits taken by these middle men but just keep on producing more and more of a product that is already in oversupply.

Why ever do they not produce less per acre but by better marketing of the product maintain the same level of sales, e.g. organic, ice cream, meat for deep freezers, farmers' markets, etc?

Farmers complain that shoppers search out the cheapest food, but rarely have they attempted to brand their products, to add value by changing the perception of their lamb, beef, milk or vegetables in the way that food manufacturers do. Produce the right product and attach it to a compelling brand image and it will sell for a good price.

Farmers are at an advantage over the food companies because by definition their products are better because they have not yet been lumped in with the rest. The naturally-produced food of the countryside is almost always superior to the highly processed product.

One in three meals that we eat is now eaten out of the home and an increasing proportion is now pre-prepared. Fewer and fewer families sit down at a table to eat together, even at the weekend.

Working mothers choose not to cook for all, and life for the young is led to a much greater extent outside the home. A vegetarian, slimming daughter on a diet buys the offerings that promise she will lose weight, while her teenage brother indulges whatever preferences he happens to have, and both eat at whatever intervals suit their mood. 'Snacking' is king. We advanced nations have ceased to take our meals in common and have descended to sequential grazing.

We are now down to only two or three cases of Foot and Mouth a day. I really do wonder how much of a cover-up is going on with the run-up to the General Election next month. The Tories are claiming one of our greatest assets is the countryside, while new Labour is claiming our NHS and education system are our greatest assets. I think one of the greatest assets of all time must be a pricing gun in a gift shop.

Sandra and Carl are thinking of selling their bungalow and buying a derelict barn with planning consent. I have been on several viewings with them and that dopey Jake. Some of the planning consents are to a very high standard and include all sorts of luxury items and fittings. One of these is a bidet – I don't know what it is but it certainly adds a touch of class.

I nearly caused an accident today and lost ever so many brownie points. The Gaffer and I were in the telescopic loader on our way to plant spuds and I noticed one of my best mates – Rover, he's an Alsatian. In my excitement to greet him I put my foot on the lever that changed the steering from two-wheel steer to crab-steer and we almost flattened the garden wall. Needless to say somebody was not very amused.

Last Autumn we planted one field with Italian Ryegrass for short term silage production. We have just mowed this field for making into round bale silage. It will be spread out on two consecutive days before being baled and wrapped. As Gareth and I were mowing this field we saw a vixen running out which probably means she has fox cubs close by.

With movement restrictions on the local hunt, and also on the pest control officers (elected and otherwise), there looks certain to be an explosion in fox numbers with disastrous consequences next lambing time.

Foot and Mouth disease is not so widespread as a few weeks ago but there are still 'hot spots' of disease in certain areas. One of these is in Powys (between Brecon and Talgarth), and another in Yorkshire. In fact Yorkshire has had 17 new cases in only nine days, which is very worrying.

It is now three months since the start of the Foot and Mouth outbreak and the livestock sector of Agriculture is still completely paralysed. No livestock markets in the country are open, there is only very limited movement of fat stock direct to slaughter (at very low prices). There seems to be only a market for about 30 per cent of our own lamb and beef – the gap being filled by imports.

Dairy farmers unable to sell their calves, beef rearers unable to purchase these calves, beef fattening units running low on numbers and unable to restock. Many beef animals going over 30 months of age and cannot be sold so still on the farms.

MAFF say farmers will be compensated for any animals that go over 30 months but I will believe this when it actually happens.

Sheep farmers are unable to sell any lambs or old ewes so numbers are building up on farms with a negative cash flow in nearly all cases. Many tack sheep still on their winter quarters, with hill farmers unable to send their sheep back out to the hill and unable to shut off any land for hay or silage. When the livestock markets do finally reopen there will be very low prices and a huge backlog of sheep so extra ewe lambs will be kept for breeding and a very real shortage of keep for the winter. Not only will stocks of hay and silage be low but any farmers who normally buy store lambs or take in tack sheep will be afraid to do so.

Farmers who normally do B&B as a means of extra income have seen this trade all but disappear.

This, without a doubt, is the worst crisis to hit UK agriculture in living memory.

In 1931, following a decade of agricultural depression, Britain abandoned free trade and introduced a measure of protection for the main farm products. Protection for farmers was consolidated in the great 1947 Agriculture Act which introduced comprehensive subsidies for a wide range of farm commodities.

Since then agricultural production has enjoyed an unprecedented measure of support, first from the national exchequer and then, in the final quarter of the 20th century, from the EU.

Subsidies greatly increased the dependence of consumers on highly processed foods, by enabling food manufacturers to buy in their raw materials at world prices. At the time of the BSE crisis of the 1990s, manufacturers at the economy end of the burger market were budgeting just 20p per kg for their meat, a target they met by making full use of mechanically recovered scraps. By choosing such products, consumers hand over control of their diets, and health, to finance directors of manufacturing companies.

Of the £60 billion that consumers spend on food, less than 20 per cent finds its way into farmers' pockets. The remainder goes to the companies that process it, package it and haul it from one end of the country to the other, or to the supermarkets that sell it. This more than anything is why the countryside is in crisis: because urban consumers spend their money with the big manufacturing corporations instead of the farmers who grow it.

Each year the CAP dispenses just over £3 billion to British farmers to encourage them to supply bog standard products, many of which are in surplus around the world, and in any case can be grown more cheaply elsewhere. 'I really do go on about things when I've got a bee in my bonnet about them, don't I'. But we really must get our own marketing sorted out.

They say a man knows he's getting old when the hairs on the inside of his nose and ears grow faster than the hairs on his head. If that's the case, the Gaffer must be at least 120. He looks like a cross between a walrus and a sea lion.

This reminds me of another restriction because of Foot and Mouth – sheep shearing. MAFF will not be issuing any licences to sheep shearers until the beginning of June. By this time a fair percentage of the lowland sheep should already have been shorn. We are keeping a very careful health check on ours against blowfly attack.

Jim and Adam, our two senior stock rams, are moaning at me every day that it's time their winter coats were removed. I remind them they are very lucky there are plenty of trees around the fields for shelter. They really do go on those two. For the last three months it's been the Gaffer, and now it's about shearing.

For the last three months everybody has been going on about burning pyres, of animals slaughtered because of Foot and Mouth. Now that the weather has turned very hot and dry – guess what? Everybody is out with the barbecues and stinking the whole street out, but nobody seems to mind. Strange lot aren't we!

Owing to the Foot and Mouth and exports cancelled, the price of lamb in France and Ireland is up 30 per cent on this time last year – it's an ill wind that blows somebody some good.

Spent most of today on a tractor with the Gaffer rolling three fields that we planted to Spring barley and undersowed a few weeks ago. It should have been rolled before it emerged but potato planting was more important. We are on a really old tractor with worn tyres and no air conditioning so I am suffering somewhat.

The herons that we kept seeing through the winter have a nest in a tree alongside the brook, which is the first time they have ever nested close to here. The only downside is that the fish stocks will be reduced but this way is probably preferable to the local poachers.

Britain has now banned all beef imports from Brazil, Argentina, Uruguay and Paraguay following outbreaks of Foot and Mouth in these countries. In the past two weeks alone, Brazil has seen five new outbreaks. It certainly makes sense when fighting the F&M fire in this country to stop sparks from other countries coming in by the back door.

The Ministry of Defence, which sources over a third of its beef for the armed forces from Brazil, Uruguay and Australia, said it would compensate for the Brazilian ban by buying more beef from Australia and New Zealand with a 'small amount' from Britain.

If you were a city-based housewife choosing between sunflower oil, olive oil and rape oil for your cooking, which would you most likely leave on the shelf? Indeed, who knows how much that ill chosen name might have influenced the critics who complain about its bright 'unnatural' colour when in flower, or its alleged allergic effects on hay fever and asthma sufferers. It is good marketing and branding practice to give what you produce an attractive name.

So let us here and now start a campaign to rename it canola, just as they have in other countries. We don't even have to think up a new name, somebody else has done it for us. It could be more important than we currently realise.

They say the difference between a good farmer and a bad farmer is a fortnight! If that is the case, it's only just after Christmas here at Faulty Farm.

Today is 26th May and all the potatoes have at last been planted and the machines bathed, oiled and put away for another season. We got an extra load of Premiere seed to plant on all the headlands, which means that, by the time we start bulking spuds into store in the autumn, all the headlands should have been lifted. Premiere is an early variety that is also suitable for early chipping.

The only serious problem we had at planting was the fertilizer. This was delivered in January, stored inside, was of British manufacture, but was damp and would not run properly through the applicator and kept blocking up and also going to powder. On a really hot sunny day it was not so bad but otherwise was a complete disaster. The application rate varied from 5 cwt to 12 cwt per acre. We had a replacement load delivered which gave no problems at all and the accuracy then was within 2-3 per cent.

The Gaffer is giving the manufacturers a really hard time and we are dreading the crop coming up to see the striping due to the blockages, and the obvious yield reduction.

Even in the present run up to the General Election the hunting debate is still rambling on. On the one side of the fence we have 'the unspeakable who pursue the uneatable', but these people do still largely understand the needs of the countryside. On the other side we have the greenies, who are led by emotions rather than common sense and generally do not have a clue as to how nature works. They have never seen the carnage in a poultry house after a visit by Reynard or helped out with lambing and seen ewes that have had their lambs stolen in the night.

The UK has the most expensive fuel of all the EU countries. In the UK, tax, including VAT, makes up 78 per cent of the price of a litre of unleaded petrol, compared to an average of 63 per cent across the other 14 EU states.

When Labour came to power in 1997 they said they would put the country back on its feet. Well, they nearly have, as it's now too costly to drive!

Government experts are now warning that milk and dairy products may be tainted by cancer-causing chemicals from Foot and Mouth pyres. They say smoke from the fires carried dioxins onto pasture grazed by dairy cattle.

The Food Standards Agency, which has issued the warning, stressed that there was no evidence yet of a build-up, and that only very few people would be at risk. A drop in milk sales could be the final blow for many farmers.

Only herds grazing within a mile and a quarter of pyres are under suspicion. Dioxins are more likely to be present in fatty products, such as whole milk, cream, soft cheese and yoghurt. The dioxins would have come mainly from the chemically treated railway sleepers used to accelerate the fires.

At the present time, stock has been slaughtered off 7,500 farms because of Foot and Mouth disease. This figure includes stock taken out under the contiguous cull.

Gareth spent part of today up a ladder cleaning out troughings that were starting to grow clumps of grass and weeds, before we have a downpour and flood some of the buildings. You'd certainly never catch me going up a ladder. It's not because I'm afraid of falling – it's the landing that worries me.

Masses of young squirrels just left their dreys at the moment, which are very easy prey to unscrupulous canines, foxes and also motorcars.

I really cannot understand humans and the attitude many of them have to racism. Myself, I am black, white and brown but I don't have a problem with it, nor do any of my mates – we are all canines. It really doesn't matter what colour a person's skin is – they are all humans after all. It seems such a shame that they cannot all live in perfect harmony.

I've been spending a few days up at Gareth's shop in the village and it is such a pleasant change from the farm.

The mere presence of a shop in a small village can add up to 10 per cent onto the value of local houses. A village with no shop or other amenities becomes like a dormitory settlement – people just come there to sleep. Village shops are good for communities – unlike supermarkets which harm them by prompting the closure of nearby smaller outlets and reducing choice. 'Supermarkets are like black holes. They suck everything around it out'.

Since the closure of all public footpaths three months ago, we have seen an absolute explosion in numbers of wildlife and nesting birds, due to one of their worst predators being banned. In fact for the first time ever, farmers and the RSPB are batting on the same side in a bid to see this trend continue. It is very unlikely that we will see a ban on the use of footpaths for three months every spring, for obvious reasons.

To help maintain this very delicate balance of nature, what we need are smaller fields, which means more hedgerows and more cover. To achieve this aim, we need more small family farms which have these smaller fields. The average field size in this area is 8-10 acres, whereas in the main arable areas it is 50 acres plus.

Scale of production is the key to profitability so one needs to get bigger to survive. Any future subsidies should not be per acre, or per breeding animal, but per family unit as a supplementary income to make small family farms viable.

Gareth had a severe tongue lashing the other day which really amused the old boy. He was spreading turkey manure on the field we cut for round bale silage and one resident who lived close by took exception to the smell. 'It's this organic farming', he said, and assured her it was going to rain in the next few days to dilute the smell.

When it comes to politics I would hardly describe the Gaffer as a bright shining light, in fact more like a 20-watt light bulb, or a flickering candle.

Vote Conservative? For most farmers that's doing what comes naturally, but the neglect and mismanagement of agriculture during the last Tory Government is too recent a memory to be easily forgiven.

Vote Liberal Democrat? If they can't be a Government they could at least try a little harder to be an opposition.

Vote Labour? It may be unfair to say that a British governing party has been so ignorant of the countryside, but nevertheless it is true.

There is, however, one issue of this election which if carried through could form the foundation stone for a farming recovery. Food from abroad is too cheap here and our food is too expensive over there. Saving the pound may tug at our heartstrings but it empties farmers' pockets.

Like it or not, the best thing on offer to farmers in this 2001 election is the prospect of a second term of this Labour Government successfully joining the Euro, at the correct exchange rate. It may seem perverse, but to survive perhaps we should vote Labour.

Rural issues featured large in the newspapers before the election was called: fuel prices, rural development, the future of MAFF, the family farm and, of course, Foot and Mouth. You name it, if it was about the countryside it was on the front page.

Now the whole country is deemed to be obsessed only with taxation, the health service, education and whether or not Ffion Hague will actually say anything during the election campaign.

At the moment Labour are way ahead in the polls. A Labour victory will mean that the British public loses out and will have voted for spin, not substance.

Politics, thanks to Bill Clinton and Tony Blair, has lost credibility with the voters and I would not be at all surprised to see a low turnout, with people switched off by the way Labour twists the truth to their own advantage. They promised to unite us, but have driven a wedge firmly between town and country, between Wales and England and Scotland and England.

If Tony Blair can ride out his Government's mishandling of the Foot and Mouth epidemic, then he will not be worried about taking on fox hunting. He will then move on to ban first shooting and then angling.

The first of the spuds that were planted are just starting to emerge, so the Gaffer is away spraying for a few days. It's too windy really so I hope he takes care with any spray drift onto susceptible crops.

Gareth and I are mowing ready for our first cut of silage. It's 26th May so we are hoping for better quality silage than last year, when the cows would not milk at all.

The grass is then spread out on two consecutive days and picked up on the third – this obviously depends on the weather. A large rake then gathers the grass into huge swaths that are gobbled up by a self propelled forage harvester and a back up team of five large tractors and trailers. Gareth does the clamp work with the telescopic handler.

Some of the grass is being hauled back from five miles away, so certain narrow lanes are best avoided at the moment. Caught a rat out of the car tyres when covering the pit, which was brilliant.

More and more people are going vegetarian with the present food scares. The Gaffer was being put in his place the other day by one of this elite band. When he commented that he was surprised she wore leather, she left in rather a hurry, probably never to return to our shop again.

All the public paths that cross our land have just had signs erected – 'Footpath Closed', a mere three months after they were in fact officially closed.

Today, 31st May, an eerie silence descended at Faulty Farm – the last of the potatoes were graded and the grading line shut down and cleaned in readiness for next year's crop.

Today, 1st June, is the first day MAFF have started to issue licences for sheep shearing and we have Gareth's mate, Lewis, and two other lads turn up to shear here at Faulty Farm. As we are still under a D Notice it is unlikely that we will be able to sell our wool, certainly not for at least 12 months.

The three lads who are shearing all farm in an area covered by a D Notice which makes it easier for them to come here shearing than if they were only in a restricted area.

They have a total of 6,000 less sheep to shear than last year because of the numbers slaughtered by Foot and Mouth. They say they are not entirely happy about going on to other farms but that they need the money this year more than ever.

Our sheep are in two batches and very thorough cleaning and disinfecting is carried out between both batches and after finishing.

Some farmers in a D Notice area are not even bothering to keep their wool, but we have decided to store ours in the hope that one day it will be saleable.

The inevitable happened today – that Jim head butted the Gaffer right in his backside. This caused him to be thrown forward and hit his head against a wall. The Gaffer ended up on the floor with Jim on top of him ready to see him off. It all happened so quickly, as I was helping to get some more ewes into the catching pen.

I leapt onto that flaming Jim and sunk my teeth into him as hard as I could which really shifted him away from the old boy. The old feller only had his pride hurt but will no doubt be more careful in future.

MAFF are proposing a 20 day standstill on stock sold through auction markets. At certain times of the year this would be disastrous for the majority of livestock farmers.

Electronic ID would do the same, without the devastating effects on livestock marketing. It would involve extra cost and work but would be a lesser evil than the 20 day standstill.

Livestock trading is getting back to normal in France. Mid-May saw most of the live markets opening for business again, albeit with a more than usual watchful eye from the state veterinary service. The markets had been closed for 10 weeks due to Foot and Mouth Disease.

A total of 1,660 cases of F&M have so far been confirmed in the UK. Farmers hit by F&M, whether in an infected area or not, can use set-aside land to graze animals. It can be grazed for the duration of the restriction and up to 30 days following the lifting of the restriction. Hay or silage can also be made off the set-aside land as long as it is for your own use, but cannot be sold.

This last fortnight has seen an enormous amount of growth of grass and all other crops. The potatoes are nearly all coming through, Winter wheat now over knee high, Spring barley catching up fast. Grass seeds that were undersown with the barley are emerging – the three undersown fields that we rolled are like a supermodel's stomach – flat and level (with nothing in it). Young crows have left their nests and are easy picking for foxes, dogs, cars, etc.

The whole country has been taken over by the forthcoming election. Protesting lorry drivers and farmers have lobbed a grenade into the campaign by disrupting fuel supplies at refineries. They are not aiming to cause fuel shortages but merely to highlight the excessive costs of motoring, by merely flexing their muscles at this stage.

Our total fuel costs here at Faulty Farm will be almost £2,000 higher this year than last. There is no way that these costs can be passed on so like most other businesses, we have to absorb them, but one cannot keep doing this for long as the profits are not there any more.

That Jim is walking around with a permanent smile on his face now that he has got even with the Gaffer, but if I were him I should be very careful that somebody does not get their own back.

Just a few years ago 'English Farmhouse' conjured up wholesome and pleasant holiday images. Not any more. The words English Farm are now associated with Foot and Mouth Disease, Mad Cow Disease, Swine Fever, fuel protestors, animal exploitation, suicide and depression. Visit an English Farm and all this can be yours!

Foot and Mouth has devastated farm tourism in this country. Farm tourism is as badly contaminated as the poor beasts in the field. Unfortunately, Summer will not happen for most of them this year and many will probably go under. Basically the public has lost faith in farms. We have all seen how farm animals are treated; how they are fed to each other, how they are trucked around the country and how they are slaughtered. Farms through the eye of the general public are no longer nice places; they are bad news.

In this country we over-react to any crisis – we 'panic bought' ourselves into a fuel crisis last Autumn because part of the tanker delivery fleet stayed put for a few days. We spent millions on solving the Millennium bug problem that never happened. The West Country turned away the biggest potential tourist bonanza of the century when it told the world the total eclipse of the sun would jam every motorway and fill every campsite in Devon and Cornwall – it never happened.

The word farm must be temporarily culled from the dictionary of countryside tourism until confidence returns. Crisis management is required at this point and it is not good tactics to use a brand that is reeling from negative images currently being shown on every TV screen and newspaper in the world.

People from abroad are asking whether it is safe to eat meat yet in the UK. Whether you could catch Mad Cow Disease by breathing the air and whether we had to burn our clothes and walk about in the white boiler suits they had seen Tony Blair wearing on TV.

We are selling lambs and beef animals for deep-freeze customers at the moment. Before moving animals off the farm all the stock must be inspected by our own vet, who then issues us with a movement licence. This movement is coordinated by MAFF who also want to know the route we take to the abattoir. MAFF also pay for the vet inspection, so all of a sudden the vets are extremely busy which must be very welcome after several months of reduced workloads and incomes.

Monday 4th June and a very early start; Tracey and I have to take Gareth to Heathrow Airport. He is off to America for two weeks to stay with one of his mates who is working out there for six months with an agricultural engineering firm, as part of his College placement scheme. Gareth flies first to Washington DC and then another plane ride to Columbus in Ohio.

As we drive along the M4 motorway, the wet Autumn and Winter combined with a late Spring means that large acreages of Winter-planted cereals are very patchy, there are more Spring-planted cereals than normal and a huge acreage is in set-aside. These factors will all contribute to a reduced yield of grain and hopefully better prices.

There do not seem to be any rabbit control measures along motorways any more with huge rabbit populations creating a possible traffic hazard, and we could see where they were grazing adjacent fields.

It never ceases to amaze me how much busier our motorways and airports seem to become every year. The thought of commuting to work in large cities every day absolutely horrifies me.

As Tracey and I drive back West along the motorway I sit in the front seat (with my seat belt on). We listen to tapes on the radio and have a really good chat with each other. We are both rather concerned as to how well the oldies will manage to run the farm without Gareth to do all the work. It will come as a hell of a shock to the Gaffer to have to do some work, but all of a sudden we are caught up with our workload, so other than milking and routine stock work, it is fairly quiet.

With just a few days to go to the General Election the whole Foot and Mouth saga has been conveniently swept under the carpet. There is, however, increased speculation that immediately after the Election there will be a return to mass culling in certain black spots. Rumour has it that extra accommodation has been booked for MAFF officials, police leave being cancelled, land being earmarked as sites for incineration and vehicles being requisitioned to transport carcasses.

If Tony Blair has delayed the slaughter of infected animals for a crucial four weeks then the people of Britain, and particularly those who live in the countryside, will not readily forgive him.

I believe the Gaffer must watch too many hospital programmes on the television, because now he fancies himself as a chiropodist. The yearling rams that we will be selling this Autumn really want their feet trimmed again and as he can't catch and turn them into a sitting position himself, he's just spent a couple of days making a 'turnover crate'. The sheep are reversed into this contraption, a lever is pulled, and they lie upside down on this kind of hammock. It certainly would not score very high marks for appearance as it is made largely out of scrap metal but it works an absolute treat. At one stage he had me as the guinea pig checking if the geometry was correct for the 'turnover' part. I am more than a little concerned about his standard of welding which is pretty awful.

Because of the urgency of completing this project I can't help but wonder if he has an ulterior motive, by getting his own back on Jim.

According to a report out this week, eggs and poultry meat are being poisoned by drugs used in intensive farming. And who do you think is behind this report – our very own Soil Association in a campaign to persuade everyone to grow and eat organic food.

Some of these associations that aim for a cleaner, greener environment can be our greatest allies or our worst nightmare depending on whether they have been influenced by the latest Government spin.

The present situation in British Agriculture cannot continue; we are not even making a living wage and no youngster in their right mind would consider being a farmer.

In the Agriculture Act of 1947 the then new Labour Government laid down a 30 year plan to double food production to enable us to feed 60 million people.

Then came our half-hearted venture into Europe – with food mountains, intervention support and quotas.

Now we have diversification, management of the environment, bed and breakfast, park keeping and of course better marketing. The next 30 years will see enormous strides in technology. By 2030 completely sustainable farming may be a necessity.

Benign (within species) genetic modification could be a reality, allowing us to grow crops that are resistant to pests and diseases and even fix their own nitrogen, removing the need for fertilizers and sprays, with all farm fuel supplied by energy crops, and less land used for agriculture overall. Vaccines for diseases such as TB, electronic movement recording, automated milking, on farm mobile slaughterhouses, no live exports, no factory farming, doubling our natural woodlands and so on.

We producers receive less than 10 pence in the pound on retail food prices. Double that, putting food prices up by less than 10 per cent, and we can farm profitably without subsidies. In exchange for one small thing – that all food consumed in this country should conform to every legal requirement under which our farmers operate. This, however, requires the political will which I fear is sadly lacking, as it contravenes World Trade organisation rules.

Today is the eve of the General Election and it's the last day of campaigning by all the political parties.

On the subject of the Common Agricultural Policy, the Tories say: 'We will renegotiate it'.

Labour says: 'We will reorientate it'.

The Lib. Dems say: 'We will reform it'.

All three of them might just as well say, 'We will work to improve the British weather'.

There is certainly plenty of scope for using, rather than abusing, the CAP – as the Irish have shown – given the necessary imagination, diplomacy and political will.

This new and larger cull of livestock after the election would actually suit MAFF quite well. Brussels wants to see a 15 per cent reduction in our livestock numbers before enlargement takes place as the ex-Eastern Bloc states join the EU, and it has even been suggested that MAFF might buy farmers out by removing their livestock and compensating them. It would be far more convenient to achieve the same ends under the smokescreen of a Foot and Mouth cull.

The Gaffer and I spent most of the day perfecting his chiropody skills on the rams. We did have one pit stop to reweld some of his fabrication that was coming apart, but otherwise the contraption works quite well. Jim and the old feller hardly take their eyes off each other for fear of who makes the first retaliatory move.

One thing that really appeals to the Gaffer is to have money coming in without doing any work. We live only half a mile from a fairly large village, are situated immediately alongside a busy road and have plenty of car parking space.

At present we are seriously considering horse livery, with the owners doing most of the feeding and cleaning out themselves, with us supplying the accommodation, bedding and feed. Rather than put up a specialist building we would partition off some of the existing ones. People really do love their horses, and it seems that everyone's horse is a hypochondriac, and their vet is their spin-doctor.

None of the locals who do livery will tell us anything about the pros and cons of the job in case we pinch any of their customers, so we are having to get in touch with people from further afield.

Had a query on our IACS Forms and, rather than try and sort it out over the phone, the Gaffer and I drive up to Llandrindod Wells to do it in person. It only took 10 minutes to sort out and was nice to meet in person the people we had been talking to over the phone for several years.

On the way up we were amazed at how much grass was in some of the fields, until it occurred to us how many stock had been slaughtered due to Foot and Mouth.

The Gaffer and I were spraying a field of Spring barley close to the village. This field had no tramlines as it had been broadcast, so we were using the blob markers to see where to drive. Had an irate phone call from a local resident to say we were killing all the seagulls. It wasn't seagulls at all but blobs of foam. I can't decide sometimes whether to be annoyed with some people or feel sorry for them.

He's back! Tony Blair that is. He's secured a historic second term in office with a landslide victory. However, only 59 per cent of voters bothered to go to the polls. William Hague has announced he will resign as leader of the Tory party as soon as a successor can be found.

Rural issues played a higher profile in this election than in previous campaigns, as the parties vied for the countryside vote. However, they had different ideas over what would appeal, with only Labour mentioning hunting in its manifesto. It really does concern me as to what will happen to my canine colleagues if they are indeed made redundant.

That Limousin bull of ours, Malcolm, is giving me cause for concern. I can't decide if he is losing his marbles or if he is a wannabe cattle dog. He runs out with the milking cows, doing what he is meant to do but when he comes into the collecting yard with the cows at milking time, he immediately drives them down the one end to the door into the milking parlour.

I really cannot decide if he thinks he is being useful by avoiding the Gaffer coming out to get the last ones in or is he just being bloody minded. I asked him what he thought he was playing at but he seems to be going through a typical teenager stage and will not give a coherent answer. We now feed him some rolled barley to take his mind off his problem, which does partly work. I think he is in serious need of counselling, but quite honestly I really do not have the time.

It is now six weeks since the weather took up at the beginning of May and the ground is getting really dry and we have a constant wind blowing. Any spraying has been really difficult because of drift onto susceptible crops.

The majority of dairy farmers have now completed their first cuts of silage before the grass comes fully into head but yields are only about two-thirds of last year's. This is partly because of the dry and windy weather, but also because the fertilizer was applied several weeks later than normal. The quality of silage is excellent but that's not much of a consolation when you can see the back wall of the silage pit at the end of February.

The first hatch of swallows have already left their nests and are flying all over the place, and are quite easy prey to unscrupulous felines who have kittens to feed.

MAFF are said to be planning to buy up sheep and beef quota – initially from farms affected by Foot and Mouth, and perhaps from non-affected farms later, as a means of reducing livestock numbers in the UK. This quota would be stockpiled in a national reserve and not re-allocated. This would push up the price of any remaining quota and make it even more difficult for small farms to survive. These plans would be welcomed by conservationists who claim too much livestock has already caused overgrazing in upland areas.

Reported cases of Foot and Mouth are now down to only two or three a day, but we must all remain vigilant for the sake of everyone's livelihood. Sheep shearing is well under way with everyone needing a licence and all contract shearers registered, but shearing could be one of the main reasons for spread. The wool has to be got off these dears and people are even suggesting that they should be dipped or sprayed with an approved disinfectant prior to shearing.

The Gaffer told me that in his younger days everybody used to wash the ewes about a week to 10 days prior to shearing to remove any grease out of the wool. They used to block a stream and throw the ewes into the water, and when he was only about 10 years old, he fell in himself and ever since has had a fear of water. Perhaps that explains why he doesn't wash his neck very often.

We have just started harvesting the first crop of 2001. Autumn-planted broad beans are just coming ready, but it is only the bottom pods that are yet big enough for picking. Gaffer, Missus and I are picking them by hand for selling in the farm shop, or the shop in the village. The price per pound is good and the pods make up about three-quarters of the weight so they are quite a luxury crop to buy, price wise. They will not be ready to let Pick-Your-Own customers on to for about two weeks by which time the strawberries will also be ready. The strawberries have already been strawed between the rows. We have a tractor-mounted straw chopper for strawing the cow cubicles in winter and by modifying the two outlets, the straw is dropped in a row behind the tractor wheels and then pulled under the plant leaves by hand.

If the weather suddenly turns wet in the next week, we will apply some slug pellets to stop these varmints feeding on the ripe strawberries.

Now that Gareth is away in America, Tracey runs the shop in the mornings from very early to 8 am and the Missus and I have to help her most days towards the end of the week when all the weekly papers appear, and also to put the extra magazines and supplements in the daily papers. Sometimes there are as many as five supplements to go into one newspaper and it takes ages.

The Missus is usually at the counter serving customers and doing orders up and Tracey is out the back sorting out these magazines. My role is general dogsbody, chief taster of canine delicacies and security officer. Tracey sometimes calls me 'General Dogsbody', which coming from her is quite acceptable, but coming from another person who I could name would not be considered quite so amusing.

Producers with stock entered under the Welfare Disposal Scheme are getting anxious to get them away before the scheme is reviewed in mid-June. Tougher entry procedures are being introduced to assess suitability and attribute priority. They would be rejected if they could go into the food chain, or go to other land. The Intervention Board say that just over one million animals have been removed under the Scheme since it first opened on 22nd March. A large number of these animals are tack sheep on lowland farms that cannot be moved back to their home farms.

There are, however, still tack sheep on farms in this area that have not as yet been slaughtered, but in excess of 50 per cent have been culled or taken home.

Under the US electoral system, its second chamber, the Senate, is made up of two elected representatives from each State, whatever the population, however rural the state. Not surprisingly the farming interest fares better in the US than the UK. Only a wholesale reform of our own second chamber, the House of Lords, under proportional representation, can give the countryside a fairer say in the governing of Britain.

Our very own National Farmers Union (NFU), which has funds in excess of £30million, rather than serving the interests of the farmers, has other vested interests. Its major investment in Tesco, Barclays Bank and the American GM giant, Monsanto, are a cause of very real concern. Tesco last year made a profit of £1billion, but it says, 'not off the backs of farmers'. Barclays Bank is accused of abandoning rural Britain by shutting down large numbers of village branches. Monsanto is experimenting with genetically modified crops when our country is not ready for it.

They almost certainly get a better return on their investment in these large companies, but I believe they should be investing in local abattoirs and small chains of butchers and grocers shops to help its members to sell their produce.

Since early man co-operated with others to help kill large animals for survival, people have been co-operating to achieve objectives that they could not reach if they acted individually. Co-operation has occurred throughout the world.

The NFU and any other countryside organisations should be the brains and part backers of co-operatives set up in virtually every county of the UK. This is one way in which our trouble-torn farming community can manage to get back on its feet, using self help and unity.

As you are probably aware, 80 per cent of subsidies are paid to 20 per cent of farmers, and I suspect that the same 20 per cent pay 80 per cent of the NFU subscriptions.

Where are the Animals Rights Activists? In this epidemic we are not talking about a few hundred hunted foxes, or mice and monkeys with shampoo in their eyes, but the sudden death of over four million cows and sheep. They should be fighting to save animals' lives, calling for vaccination, or picketing MAFF to get their act together.

They would have the support of millions of animal lovers. They could throw off their balaclavas, defuse their bombs, send out leaflets on vegetarianism or take in the border collies that have lost their jobs.

The Animal Liberation Front says animal life is more precious than human life and yet they sit back and watch the slaughter. This proves they don't really care about animals, but just want to promote class warfare against toffs and drugs' conglomerates.

The Gaffer has a mastery of the English language like a Rubik Cube. With just one word he reduces that flaming Jim from a lean, mean, fighting machine to a nervous wreck. He now calls him Kebab.

Agriculture Secretary Nick Brown and the Ministry of Agriculture have both been axed by Tony Blair. MAFF is being replaced by a new Department for the Environment Food and Rural Affairs (DEFRA) which will be headed up by Margaret Beckett. The word Agriculture is no longer mentioned.

Sparrow hawks and buzzards do not eat ham sandwiches, they eat sparrows, yellowhammers, skylarks and any other birds they get their sights on – and are very good at it.

The increase in these predatory birds, currently protected by law, is being blamed for the decline of songbirds. Magpie numbers are also at an all time high and these also get the blame for being cold-blooded murderers.

To blame farmers for increased use of pesticides is extremely naïve considering we only use 80 per cent of the sprays we used five years ago. With corn at about half the price it was then, we cannot afford insurance spraying.

It is now illegal to remove hedgerows without consent (which is almost impossible to obtain) and all farmers are really into tree planting and conservation. Personally I think the numbers of songbirds has increased in the last two or three years.

After fetching the cows in for milking in the evenings, I mostly have a snooze under the trees in the lawn. The other evening, about halfway through milking, I could hear a noise like a tap being turned on and off and water cascading down a roof. On investigating I notice that a joint had come adrift in the milk pipe carrying the milk across to the bulk tank. I alerted the Missus who told the Gaffer, but by this time there was milk everywhere. A screwdriver and jubilee clip soon remedied the problem. The old feller's philosophy is, 'if it ain't broke, don't fix it', which often is not the best approach.

We went over to see Sandra, Carl and that smoothie Jake the other night. They have a water feature out the back with a fountain. This fountain was not working properly, so 'macho man' decided to repair it. Within minutes he had broken a water pipe and he got absolutely drenched. At Faulty Farm we have no immediate neighbours so the curtains are never drawn. Anyway 'macho man' was in a bedroom of their bungalow changing into some dry clothes (with the curtains open) when a coach load of tourists pulled up outside to go to into the pub across the road. The sight of the old feller with no clothes on was probably more of a deterrent to visiting the countryside than the Foot and Mouth epidemic. You should have heard the cheering. We sometimes go into the pub for a drink but that evening there was no way he was going to.

For a number of years here at Faulty Farm we have talked of making a nature trail around the farm, to incorporate areas of woodland, water courses, ponds, fishing, badger-watching, bird nesting, the dairy cows, calves, sheep, PYO crops, etc. Apart from the logistics of creating the course so as to cause minimal disruption to grazing the dairy herd, there is the fairly mammoth task of making and erecting signs without causing undue confusion. A sign – 'an old buzzard lives here' – could really only mean one person.

Today I asked one of our more affluent cows 'Are you limping a little, my dear?' 'No Benny' she replied, 'I'm limping a lot'.

We really do need the foot trimmer here for a day, and the sooner the better. Because we are still under a D Notice we do not feel it is correct to ask one to come onto our farm, for obvious reasons. The other alternative is to buy our own foot-trimming crush, which is expensive, and these qualified guys are so good at their job it does seem a bit of a luxury.

Saw a fascinating programme on the telly last night about sheep dog trials – entitled 'One Man and His Dog'. Almost simultaneously to the dog moving in different directions, he had the man whistling commands, and at the end, to get the sheep into the pen, these dogs had trained their man to open and shut the gate. It really must have taken years of practice. I don't think it would ever be possible to train my man to be so obedient. The programme really should have been renamed 'One Dog and His Man'.

Gareth phoned up today from America. I didn't have time to talk to him, but the Gaffer was on the phone to him for ages. He's hired a car this week and gone 'drive about'.

He says that farming in the States is not very profitable. Like us they have 2001 costs at 1975 prices. He's driven through Ohio, Virginia, Carolina, Tennessee, Kentucky and Indiana. Most of the farms are four to five hundred acres which is not enough to live off, so the farmers and or their wives go out to work.

The grub is first class with huge helpings which seems to appeal to him. Unfortunately the lad is getting more like his old man every day. He went by the White House in Washington to have tea with President Bush but unfortunately he was not in residence.

Jim is just starting to regain his confidence after the old boy called him Kebab, which was a bit below the belt really. Jim says the Gaffer is as much use as an ejector seat in a helicopter, and not many people would refute that.

Within just one week of Tony Blair being returned to power he is set to outlaw foxhunting. Pro-hunting groups fear the Government will attempt to steamroller through a new Bill to kill off hunting even if the Lords oppose it.

It would appear to have more to do with class prejudice than with sensible Government. However, any new legislation Bill would almost certainly contain 12 months' delay before implementation, allowing hunts to wind up their affairs.

As predicted a few weeks ago when the Foot and Mouth epidemic was being swept under the carpet, the confirmed cases per day is now back up to eight or ten. So all of a sudden we are back to reality that agriculture and country tourism are bad news.

It is now 11 weeks since we were served a D Notice here at Faulty Farm with still no word of when it will be lifted. There is a small slaughterhouse in the village which is the only place that we can kill fat cattle or sheep (assuming we have a buyer). We cannot move them out of a D Notice area. Right across the country frustration is growing at what appears to be unnecessary delays in lifting restrictions. DEFRA blame a shortage of testing facilities. Farmers are more inclined to point the finger at a lack of political will on the one hand, and administrative inefficiency on the other.

Some British companies with farmer shareholders absolutely amaze me with their stupidity. Dairy Crest are offering cut price New Zealand lamb with their franchised doorstep deliveries, at a time when our own lamb cannot be exported meaning that it could be purchased for virtually the same price. The National Sheep Association chief executive John Thorley described the promotion as 'absolutely diabolical'. Our NFU made no comment.

The light hill lambs, such as the Swaledale and Welsh Mountain will be the most difficult to place this Autumn as the Southern European markets will be unavailable. As a back up the sheep industry is looking at private storage aid and purchase for destruction schemes.

As of today (16th June, 2001) latest figures show 3.32 million animals have been culled or identified for culling in the Foot and Mouth epidemic. In addition 1.1 million animals have been culled under the Livestock Welfare Disposal Scheme. Estimated compensation cost is £768 million.

Only a third of farmers are in favour of joining the single European Currency despite the fact that the strength of sterling has substantially cut support payments in recent years. Personally I think farmers should concentrate on the economic rather than the emotional reasons for their support of the Euro.

A third of farmers had increased their overdraft in the last year with nearly a quarter taking out a new loan. Over half of farmers do not have a successor for their business and so would obviously favour a farmer retirement scheme. 40 per cent of farmers are not making a profit.

The Gaffer is very adept at giving advice. He tells Gareth there are three qualities to avoid in a girl: (1) blonde hair (2) driving a Range Rover and (3) a love of horses. He says with these three qualities you would have a superb sex life, but after 10 years she would clear off with half your farm! It sounds like being trapped between a rock and a hard place to me.

With organic farming becoming more popular, one of the main requirements is establishing clover in grassland. Ploughing and reseeding is probably the surest method but is expensive and takes the field out of production for several months. Broadcasting the seed and scratching the surface depends on the weather and competition from the existing sward. Slot seeding in an organic situation provides a major highway for slugs.

Now very small quantities of seed are mixed with the cattle feed and are excreted unharmed in the dung. The dung pat suppresses the grass, dries out and produces a perfect medium for seed growth. The seed is mixed with the feed in May, June and July and works out at less than 50p per cow with superb results.

We hear so much these days of anorexia. Well the Gaffer suffers from something completely different – Excessorexia. If the so-and-so didn't eat so much he would not have such a big gut on him.

The Countryside Alliance is giving the Government one month to demonstrate to rural Britain that they care, that they will enable rural Britain to sort out its own future and will not get in the way of people who want to live their lives in freedom.

If these objectives are not being seen to be met, we are having a Countryside March in London this Autumn, in place of the cancelled event that was scheduled to be held on 17th March.

It's just after the middle of June and we have had about 50 mm of rain in the last couple of days, which was desperately needed, for the grassland and all other crops. It means we have had to spread slug pellets onto the strawberries, but it's nice to see the cattle and sheep having extra grass to eat. The dairy cows have been buffer fed round bale silage for the last two weeks and we will continue this practice all Summer.

We are really busy getting ready for the PYO, with strimming, knapsack spraying, sweeping the yards and generally tidying up. In fact I seem to have no spare time at all, and I don't sleep very well standing up.

My town dwelling canine friends tell me how lucky I am to be living in the country because of lack of stress. Us country folk are said to be immune to this new and trendy ailment. It attacks only city dwellers without warning, especially if you are in heavy traffic, have an important job in an office in a city, or work for the Government. Many of these affected people attend courses to transform them into the touchy, feely, meditating, candle burning types they have become today.

The old word for this new condition was worry. Because we live in the country away from everything stressful, we have no worries. We spray our crops to prevent diseases, inject our livestock to keep them healthy, pollute the countryside with our high-tech farming practices and rely on EU subsidies to supplement our already vast incomes. Sounds idyllic doesn't it.

Back in the early Spring I had a clandestine association with a very attractive female collie belonging to one of the Gaffer's mates. They turned up here in their pick-up and he spent an hour drinking tea and talking to the Gaffer, while this gorgeous young thing and myself had our wicked way with each other. I can't decide if it was love, lust or our natural instinct to procreate. However, they turned up again today with five young puppies in the back of their vehicle, and some handsome devils they were.

Apparently this was a set-up job and we have been promised the pick of the litter in exchange for my contribution. I feel like I have been taken advantage of like some super-sire, when all along I thought it had been conducted with the utmost secrecy.

After a series of tests of intelligence we decide on this one young lad as my assistant, but he will not be coming here for at least six months to allow them time to partly train him. I can't help but think I could train him as well myself in the art of pest control, but there are, however, other aspects of a working dog's CV. I really am so chuffed it is unbelievable.

Gareth arrived home from America today. He got a coach from Heathrow to Chepstow, which was much cheaper than Tracey and I fetching him.

He had a superb time and also went into Canada by way of Niagara Falls. He covered over 4,000 miles in a hire car so saw a reasonable amount. He was stopped for speeding – doing 73 mph in a 50 mph area, but they let him off. Perhaps they were afraid of catching 'Hoof and Mouth' off him.

The highway patrol cars have a radar gun fixed in their cars and they can record your speed as you are driving towards them, when they are still driving. They then turn around, chase after you with blue lights flashing and book you.

Have a cow today that has torn one of her teats, probably on barbed wire. The Missus gets on the phone to the vet and who do you think turns up? Big Ally. He is reluctant to get out of his car until the Gaffer comes in case I have a go at him. They are up in the milking parlour sewing and taping the teat back up with his car parked on the yard with the boot open. I was seriously considering making a deposit on top of his medicines but think it would be more worthwhile the day after I have eaten a takeaway, so I am saving that one for another time.

It's 21st June and the longest day of the year. The old feller says that on this date the potatoes should be touching across the rows. The silly sod is on his hands and knees pulling the plants towards each other to see if they will touch, but no way! Some of the later-planted ones are only just through the ground.

We have just had another week of baking hot temperatures and all crops are really suffering from drought stress. The Gaffer is hopeful of having a poor potato yield and some reasonable prices. He says you never make any money out of spuds if you have a good yield, as the prices are invariably low and here at Faulty Farm we cannot irrigate.

The livestock markets have just reopened in Ireland after the Foot and Mouth restrictions, with some excellent prices being obtained.

The first case of Foot and Mouth in Wales for nearly four weeks has just been confirmed near Brecon. The family concerned have grazing rights on the Brecon Beacons and also another range of common land, so the implications for the surrounding area are horrendous.

We are now into the Pick Your Own Seasonwith strawberries and broad beans for picking with other crops catching up fast. About 75 per cent of the picking is done on a Saturday and Sunday so the last thing we need now are a series of wet weekends.

On a Sunday afternoon some families with large numbers of kids turn up, not so much to pick, but to have a free feed of strawberries. We can spot them coming a mile off and send them to a weedy part of the field that we have finished picking, so they have to work really hard to fill up.

These families nearly always have a dog that has to stay in the car. After I have spent half an hour barking at this yapping dog and jumping up at the window and scratching the paintwork on the doors of the car, none of them ever come again. 'Bad strawberries and a crazy dog' are their reasons, not knowing that we have set them up.

I've still got this problem with bad breath, so now I have to take these tablets that taste like a mint with a hole in the middle – you know the one I mean. Because they are tablets and I am not supposed to like tablets, I make a hell of a fuss of taking them but in fact they taste quite nice. I think they are called Niagara – when I first saw the label I thought it was Viagra and I certainly do not need those, not yet anyway.

You may find it hard to believe but today we had a lamb born out of one of the ewe lambs that we purchased at the end of January. Nobody is taking the blame but I notice that Jim has a smile on his face. The gestation period for a sheep is 147 days so it would just coincide.

This is the time of year for village fetes and Vicar's tea parties and we seem to be quite heavily involved with these fundraising activities. Most years there's a competition to 'guess the weight of the sheep', and yes, you've guessed, it's that flaming Jim who spends all day in a pen being poked and prodded and loving the publicity.

This year because of Foot and Mouth disease, having sheep at the event was not an option so instead they are having a competition to guess the weight of the dog. My name has been put forward but because I am not very big, they have decided to guess the combined weight of two dogs. Well the other dog is a great big Alsatian and I have heard it rumoured that he is gay. The thought of spending an afternoon in a sheep pen in the middle of the village green with a bent dog is not my idea of heaven.

I am eyeing up this great hulk with limp wrists and carrying a handbag and thinking to myself, be careful buddy boy, you start messing with me and you'll end up firing blanks or maybe nothing at all. After about an hour he made his move, I am backed right into a corner. I tolerated his familiarity for quite some time before making my move – thinking Marsh Mallows, Marsh Mallows and clamped my jaws shut around his lower regions. He gave an enormous yelp and jumped clean out of the pen with me still holding on. Straight through the middle of the egg and spoon race we ran, causing absolute chaos.

I eventually let go and was coaxed back into the Land Rover by the missus who made a generous donation in exchange for the money I should have raised. I am certainly not flavour of the month in the village at the moment, but the Gaffer thought it highly amusing. I can just see the headlines in next month's newsletter – 'Dog wins egg and spoon race with two stones handicap'.

That doyen of the organic movement – the Soil Association are floundering like a ship without a mast. Stuffed into a national newspaper supplement last week was a Soil Association flyer. On one side was a photograph of a yard of cows, mostly dead, with the headline 'There's no such thing as cheap food'. On the other side was an invitation: 'Help us change the face of British Farming for £3 per month'.

However, this was not a campaign against the imports of cheap meat which brought Foot and Mouth to these shores and reduced British Agriculture to the impoverished state where a campaign to save it is needed.

It blames F&M, BSE and pesticides in water on farmers who have been encouraged to cut corners in the quest for cheaper food. The Soil Association used to perform an admirable task, so I am appalled that it should lend its name to this sort of rubbish.

BSE was caused by the renderers and feed compounders, or more likely organo phosphorus (OP) products for warble fly control. Pesticide residues were caused largely by large agrochemical firms; F&M by imports of meat from countries where the disease is endemic, and the lack of policing of import controls that are supposed to be in place.

Just lately Gareth and I have spent many hours picking wild oats out of the cereal crops by hand, but with an ulterior motive. This is to acquire an ability to follow tramlines and walk through standing crops of cereals without leaving any trace that you have been there. This is so that we can participate in one of the favourite Young Farmers' activities of this time of year – the making of Crop Circles.

Three of Gareth's mates and himself have had several meetings drawing up complex patterns to try and outdo their efforts of previous years. They have studied maps of Foot and Mouth restricted areas, public footpaths and farms with livestock enterprises. They prefer to go down into Wiltshire near ancient burial sites or places of archaeological interest to add authenticity.

Nearly always they manage to strike a deal with the farmer involved on condition that if he charges people to look at the circles, any money goes to a worthwhile charity.

The five of us set off from here an hour before dark with folding ladders, planks of wood, ropes, pegs etc. We arrive at the site at about 10.30 and immediately set to work. My job is lookout and if anyone approaches the car I make a noise like a fox crying to alert the lads and not cause suspicion to the prowlers.

Some of the more complex designs we are making this year take the four of them between four and five hours at the end of which time the lads are completely bushed.

It's back home by four o'clock just as it is starting to get light. They carry bags of party clothes for an alibi in case of being stopped by the police, who must wonder why ever take a dog to a party – perhaps I am a party animal!

One of the most interesting aspects of this charity work of ours is studying the newspapers and news reports a few days later to see if the 'croppies' (an assorted group of corn circle hunters, investigators and experts) think it is a fake, whirlwind or eddies, aliens, electromagnetism – or even the sexual excitement of animals.

We are considered to be one of the better groups of hoaxers and on occasion have even been invited to display our talents, to which we always agree as long as a worthwhile charity benefits. However, not going to bed at night means the next day you feel as if you have been to hell in a handcart.

A field of ryegrass has been cut for the second time with the intention of making it into small bale hay for a horse customer. Unfortunately the Gaffer is one of these fussy hay makers who likes to wash his hay, and sure enough the day before it was due to be baled, the weather turned cooler with showers so we have a contractor in to round bale and wrap it.

Isn't modern technology marvellous? The Gaffer and myself are rowing up this silage, and alongside us is this huge tractor towing a round baler with a chopping mechanism and towed behind is a bale wrapper which is wrapping a bale as the next one is being formed in the baler. All very impressive, and computer controlled, with a television screen in the cab keeping an eye on the wrapping process.

Due to the slaughterhouses killing stock under the Welfare Disposal Scheme, it is now over three months since any over 30-month-old cattle have been slaughtered, resulting in a backlog of over 200,000 barren cows trapped on farms. These are eating into next Winter's already short forage supplies. It also means farmers are not going to start buying in replacements until they have got rid of these animals they already have.

To date there are 1,793 cases of Foot and Mouth since the first outbreak was reported more than four months ago. Three more cases were confirmed yesterday with experts predicting that cases are likely to continue through the summer.

DEFRA said the average payment to farmers is £116,000. Total compensation payments to farmers who have lost animals to Foot and Mouth disease are very nearly £1billion. This figure already dwarfs the £11.5 million, which had been paid out in BSE compensation by April last year, with more Foot and Mouth payments expected.

It is also estimated that veterinary bills and testing of farm animals will cost around £79 million, while £195 million will have to be spent on cleaning and disinfecting farms and £152 million on transport and disposal of carcasses. 3.5 million animals have been culled to stop the spread of the disease, and a further 1.1 million under the welfare scheme. Just over 8 per cent of UK livestock has been culled so far according to official DEFRA statistics. Stock has so far been culled off 8,000 farms.

Welsh speaking farmers have been amused by the fact that the acronym for the new Department of the Environment, Food and Rural Affairs – DEFRA – is the same word for 'wake up' in Welsh.

Sunday 1st July and we have a phone call from DEFRA to say that our Form D Restrictions have been lifted. Here at Faulty Farm we have been under a Form D for a total of 13 weeks. Compared to many people we were not too badly affected. Our biggest problem is having sheep here and making us short of grass for the cows to graze. We have been buffer feeding the cows for over a month so are already eating into next Winter's supply of forage.

We are now under Form E Restrictions which are much easier to live with. We have applied for a licence to move the sheep to some off-lying land that was cut for silage five weeks ago where there is more than adequate grazing. However, the weather is staying very hot and dry with all crops showing signs of stress.

The Gaffer has modified the cab of his sprayer tractor so now I can go along when he sprays the spuds and corn. The only modification that occurred was to clean out most of the rubbish that had built up in the cab. It's not perfect but does make for an exciting day out. Especially today when we had a blowout in the front tyre and with the front tank full as well we were suddenly going nowhere. It really was one hell of a bang – I thought the rabbits were shooting at us.

He gets on the phone to Gareth who takes a front wheel off another tractor and soon we are mobile again.

The spuds are suffering from the dry conditions and only about 50 per cent of the acreage is yet meeting across the rows. Unless we have some rain soon some of the dry patches never will meet across the rows.

As well as the blight spray we are applying some foliar feed – not the most efficient means of fertilising, but does help in difficult growing conditions. This foliar feed we are using contains seaweed extract so I am expecting to see hordes of seagulls.

Talking of seagulls – we live about 20 miles from the coast and only see two or three seagulls a week yet within 20 minutes of starting ploughing in the Spring or Autumn hundreds of them appear as if from nowhere. Apparently this used to happen before mobile phones were the norm, so what communication system do they use?

Most weeks when I have time I go to the Cash and Carry in Cardiff with Gareth in the van. The amount of pop and drinks we are selling in the shop at the moment is just unreal. Something else the lad bought this week which you won't believe – a pallet full of toilet rolls. I can't decide if they were at the right money or are they having a curry party here in the village?

It's at this time of the year that the 'yellow peril' appears – Ragwort. These tall erect plants with yellow flowers appear on our banks and verges as if by magic. The down side is that they are extremely poisonous – especially after cutting.

Most local authorities now spend huge sums of money employing people to pull these weeds by hand and gradually we are seeing a reduction. However, in a bid to cut costs, verges were not cut on a regular basis for 10 years or so which allowed for the increase of this dangerous invader. Many a horse, and indeed other animals, have died through eating hay containing ragwort.

The Spring barley although only planted eight weeks ago, is already out in head – so in about another eight weeks time will be ready for combining. Because we were late planting we increased the seed rate which means a thicker crop, more humidity on the lower leaves, and a high incidence of mildew. So today we are spraying with fungicide to reduce the mildew infection.

Because of the late planting the crop is literally racing through its growing stages and the ears are noticeably smaller than in a normal season. I see several rabbits running in the crop but because the corn is now twice my height it is rather pointless me chasing them – not only would I not be able to catch them, but these barley awns seem to get in all the wrong places.

Several local farmers have planted fields of stubble turnips which are really struggling, not only with the drought but also with flea beetles. These are small green/black beetles that you can see hopping around and if they attack the plants at the seedling stage, within days they will eat the whole crop as it is emerging. Seed dressings have been banned so a very careful eye needs to be kept on the crop and spraying may be necessary.

Before the advent of sprays and monogerm seed all root crops required a huge amount of labour – hand hoeing for weed control and singling the crop. In the early 1960s, when the Gaffer was a student on a farm, all the staff were given two weeks holiday for piece-work hoeing of sugar beet, and by working very long hours he could earn up to £30 a week which seemed a fortune in those days.

The basic agricultural wage was 10 pounds and 10 shillings (£10.50) per week of 48 hours. It cost £25 to tax a vehicle, petrol was 3 shillings and 9d. a gallon, a new mini-van cost him £375 and he could fill the tank with petrol for £1. Vehicles were very basic in those days and a wing mirror was an optional extra, no seat belts were fitted and annual MOTs had not been heard of. How times have changed! With the current state of British farming he would probably be pleased to earn as much as £30 a week now. I really don't know why he doesn't try writing a book to supplement his income, but he is probably far too damn thick.

I can't really decide if the sheep here alongside the house are becoming more obedient or am I becoming more proficient in the art of sheep handling. Sometimes I even think I could become a TV star if I had a different trainer to the Gaffer – his language would not really be suitable for early evening viewing.

We really do live in a topsy turvey world. On the one hand we have the Government telling us that the Foot and Mouth virus is spread by the wind. This same Government then claims that pollen from GM crops stays obediently where it is told. Just whom are we to believe?

The Government is not keen to hold a public enquiry into the Foot and Mouth epidemic that has laid waste to Britain's farming and tourist industries. How much more evidence of incompetence might emerge from the public inquiry? Indecision and panic marked the Government's handling of the disease.

Tony Blair allowed himself to be influenced into the idea of vaccinating animals on farms neighbouring those infected, instead of slaughter. Still hoping to hold the election on the chosen date of 3rd May, the Prime Minister was naively hoping vaccination would supply a magic solution to what had become a political as well as an agricultural problem.

That idea was shot down when farmers' leader Ben Gill asked the question: Would the supermarkets agree to sell milk from vaccinated animals? No one at Downing Street had even thought of it.

The only organisation that emerged with credit from the whole embarrassing business was the Army. While MAFF officials dithered, citing shortage of resources for their failure to implement their own 24 hour cull of infected animals, the Army used the Yellow Pages to find contractors and equipment to bury the thousands of slaughtered animals, even buying the entire stock of mobile phones from one shop to get round a shortage of telephone lines.

A measure of Tony Blair's anger and embarrassment over Foot and Mouth is that immediately the election was over, he abolished MAFF and demoted Minister of Agriculture, Nick Brown. Will Blair now bring himself to hold the inquiry the countryside wants? Personally I think not, but time will tell.

The 5th July and our licence has come through to move the sheep to some off-lying land. A Ministry vet comes to inspect the stock to be moved and check that the cattle trailer was properly cleaned and disinfected. He then followed the vehicle with all the loads we moved. The vet this time was from South Africa so we had an interesting talk about farming in his country.

The only sheep we still have here at home are Jim and Adam, the two senior stock rams and the yearling rams that are due to be sold this autumn.

Aventis are offering £1,000 a hectare to farmers for GM crop trial tests this coming winter. I think everyone living within a six mile radius should have a chance to vote on whether or not they want the proposed trial to go ahead.

Now that our Form D notice has been lifted we are at last able to sell some stock. Last September we bought some cull ewes to fatten for sale in March when the price is normally good. With the exception of a few that lambed the rest have been kept for 10 months for nothing. They cost £11 each in the Autumn and we will be lucky to get any more for them now. Because the Foot and Mouth restrictions came in after the start of the retention period, we could not even get any quota for them. We did try to get them moved under the Welfare Disposal Scheme, but not very hard, as in future years DEFRA is bound to reduce your quota or Stocking Density Limits as a consequence.

The vet had to check out all the stock 24 hours prior to movement and it was a very early start at 4.30 am to get loaded and to the abattoir by our allotted time. DEFRA also tell you the route you have to take to avoid certain areas that may be contaminated or clean.

We have also managed to sell a lorry load of store cattle – mostly continental heifers that are just ready for bulling, but the price is not very exciting. To find a buyer we contacted several auctioneers who put us in touch with prospective purchasers.

Got stocked up with Yorkie Bars today ready for a long drive. Every year the Gaffer, Missus and myself go up to Scotland to see the seed potatoes growing that we will be planting next year. In fact it's really an excuse to have a break for a few days and to experience the wonderful hospitality of his Scottish mates.

On the drive up we are amazed at how much stock has been culled in certain areas due to Foot and Mouth. The first port of call is a farm near Inverness where the Gaffer worked for one Easter holidays when he was in Agricultural College. He and his college mate went up to lamb these 700 ewes and he still says he did not believe one could wear so many clothes and still be cold – hardy lot the Scots. I don't know if it was the change of air or too much drink, but the old boy offered to buy a round of drinks which is almost unheard of.

We then made our way across to the eastern side of Scotland to see the seed potato growers. There really is some fine land around these parts and all the crops we saw looked superb. One of the farms we visited had an 18-year-old son who had been accepted to do a degree course in Agriculture at a very well known and respected Agricultural college on the Cotswolds. He is looking to work for one year on a farm in the South of the country and it sounds as if he may even be coming to work at Faulty Farm. The guy must be mad.

I don't know if the Gaffer was trying to impress them or what, but once again he offered to buy a round of drinks – that's twice in three days; must be a record!

This lad has a mop of ginger hair and talks very fast in a broad Scottish accent, and I had difficulty understanding him. He's looking to start the job at the end of the year and is coming down to see us in the late autumn – I don't think he will be very impressed.

It really was a nice break and the Gaffer hardly moaned for four days which is a hell of an improvement.

I really do wish these motorway service stations would make better provisions for us travelling canines, in the way of a few more trees and recreational areas.

The evening after we got back home, Tracey, Moose, Gareth and a few of their mates have a barbecue on this patio area out the back of the shop in the village. Anyway, by climbing on top of the wall I get a good view of the top end of the pub car park which is quite badly lit. In one of the cars is a young couple unaware that they were being observed. It really was so embarrassing, I just did not know where to look – I ended up having to shut one eye. Hardly what I would call safe sex – if her father had caught them he would have killed the guy.

There are still two or three outbreaks of Foot and Mouth being confirmed every day in different parts of the country. There has not been a new case at Brecon in Powys now for a week and up to 15,000 sheep on the Brecon Beacons are being tested with encouraging results so far.

The Army is being used to round up and pen various flocks of hefted sheep belonging to graziers who have grazing rights on the mountain. These hefted flocks graze the same areas in which they were born but are not fenced in.

Back in March members of the Government's scientific committee were unanimously advocating vaccination. The Government accepted this advice, but now is completely opposed to it because the supermarkets have said they will not sell meat or milk from vaccinated animals. Voluntary vaccination by individual farmers is illegal.

As from 1st July it is now illegal to bury or dispose of any cattle over the age of 30 months that die. DEFRA must be informed and they will be taken away by approved contractors and tested for BSE to see what remains in the national herd.

Lord Whitty, Junior Minister at DEFRA, warned that farmers could not expect taxpayers to carry on baling them out for losses caused by the disease. Well! Have you ever heard of such arrogance in your life! Why do we have BSE – because of the Government allowing the temperature to be dropped in the rendering process of meat and bone meal; and who wanted to feed meat and bone meal anyway? - the feed companies, certainly not the farmers. And another thing – people have been spreading meat and bone meal on their gardens for generations, but no mention of CJD from eating rhubarb or vegetables. And why not a public enquiry of OP's (compulsory warble fly dressing of cattle for years) to see if these are the cause – new evidence makes it look increasingly likely, but it won't happen as insurance payouts to victims would bankrupt the pharmaceutical companies.

Why do we have Foot and Mouth disease? No farmer has brought it into the country – it has entered because of lack of import controls, and even after paying out over £1 billion in compensation these still have not been tightened. It's high time Lord Whitty took his blinkers off and started living in the real world and stopped blaming the farmers and started looking at, and taking steps to prevent the same thing happening again in a few years' time.

Pick-Your-Own is progressing quite well – because of the very hot weather last week the strawberries ripened very quickly and we had to pick more than normal for sale in the shop. Also because it was so hot people were not coming to pick in the heat of the day but were more likely to come in the early morning or late evening. Raspberries, gooseberries and blackcurrants are also now ready as are peas and broad beans. Now that the strawberries have virtually finished what we have now are what we call the 'serious pickers' – these will sit on a milk or pop crate under a blackcurrant bush and pick for hours.

Two families managed to lock their keys in their car which is about average. I ended up having two serious dog fights – I won the first but was given a hell of a beating by the other, again this is about average. The owner of the dog that gave me a hiding comes in regularly for spuds and ready picked fruit and veg. We call him ruggy because he has this rug growing on this face – a beard. Anyway yesterday when he left his car door open I went in and made a fairly substantial deposit in the back of his car. I am hoping he blames his own dog and will give him some serious grief.

Sandra and Carl have gone to Canada for two weeks, and yes, you've guessed it – we have that upper class twit Jake staying here. I still can't make the guy out. He won't back me in a dog fight, I can't get him interested in any ratting, he just wants to sleep and eat all day. The only time he comes alive is when our neighbour puts his banger to work to frighten the crows off his corn.

Due to the lack of rainfall this last two months, there have been a few thunderstorms but we seem to have missed most of them, there is a very real shortage of grass. This is especially so in the case of organic farms.

Nowadays it's all sell, sell, sell. One electricity company who kept ringing and wanting to save us money and book an appointment, when asked by the Gaffer what precautions they were taking against Foot and Mouth and were they avoiding infected areas, were most indignant – they did not think it was their job to look on the Internet to check. In fact they were so engrossed on making their bonuses they had conveniently overlooked Foot and Mouth. After the rocket the Gaffer gave them they just may start acting more responsibly.

What's your opinion of these metric weights we now have to abide by? In a recent survey one-third of people did not understand it at all, one-third had to convert to imperial to understand and one third say they do understand it. In fact 75 per cent of all shoppers support shopkeepers who continue to sell in pounds and ounces in defiance of the law. Here at Faulty Farm we have not converted because the Gaffer would never understand it. It's taken him 30 years to get used to decimal currency.

About 32 per cent of our lamb, worth £315 million is exported every year. These are mainly the lighter lambs from the later lambing and smaller hill breeds. Spain, Italy and France takes the majority of these lambs.

With Foot and Mouth and no export market we are starting to see a vast oversupply in the UK with prices down to £1.40 per kilo (which is about two-thirds of last year's price). Up to three million newborn lambs may have to be shot to prevent a slump in the price of British meat. They will then be buried in pits already dug for infected carcasses, under proposals now being worked out between farmers' leaders and Government Ministers. Farmers will get paid £10 per head for each animal, while the Government will pick up the bill for disposal.

Experts are saying that we could lose 50 per cent of the lambs in this country and it wouldn't make a scrap of difference to market prices, simply because so much is coming in from abroad.

As well as this purchase for destruction scheme, plans are being looked at to opening a private storage scheme in September and October. However, this frozen meat would then be dumped on the market next Spring just as prices are starting to rise, so it would be a complete disaster.

Today is 15th July, which is St Swithin's Day. If it rains today it will rain for the next 40 days. We got a few showers but nothing serious. In the last four days the weather has been quite unsettled with about two inches of rain and more rain forecast for the coming week.

Two of our set-aside fields left in green cover since last year have been cut and round baled for feeding to our own stock (a concession for this year only due to F&M). We then went in with a heavy set of trailed discs, power harrowed and planted forage rape for grazing by sheep later in the Winter. The seed costs less than £5 per acre and the present rain will make for quick germination and smothering of any weeds. Not that weeds are really a problem at this time of year anyway.

One of the most troublesome weeds of all is Fat-Hen. If these germinate in the spring and are not controlled through June and July, in good conditions they can grow by up to a foot a week and completely smother a crop, reaching up to six feet in height. Fortunately they are fairly easy to control with careful management – needless to say we have more than our fair share at this farm.

The Gaffer, Tracey, Missus and myself are off to the seaside for the day, so pack the bucket and spade and the shades and it's away we go. We tried to talk the old boy out of coming to avoid his moaning and not only that, he is expensive to run on a day out. He just keeps pigging out non-stop, burgers, ice cream, donuts, chips, candyfloss – anything that the big kid can get down his gullet.

Get to our destination and boy, is it hot – his first stop is a pub to quench his thirst. Get to the beach and, disaster – signs up saying 'no dogs allowed on the sand', even on a lead. I never did like going on a lead anyway. We decide that the oldies and Tracey go on ahead and I follow at a distance so nobody knows who I belong to, but to be careful not be caught by the wardens or deck chair attendants. If they think I have lost sight of them the Gaffer just has to whistle to let me know where they are.

The beach is really crowded and some of the nubile young ladies are lying face down on the sand with their straps undone. By running over their backs I cause instant exposure of their prized assets, loud shrieks, and rounds of applause from younger male sunbathers. Talk about silicone – I always thought Silicone Va ey was in California but certainly not all of it.

The Gafi r thought this part of my training was great sport so he had me going in front of him so he could get a better view.

Not very long before the spoilsports arrive – a bloody great posse of officials chasing me. This is where my real prowess kicks in. Not only am I in much better physical condition than these beach bums, but I also have four-wheel drive compared to their two. At one stage there were six of them chasing me, but by running over the appropriate female persons they were so distracted that they soon fell way behind.

To cool off I headed down to the water's edge and nearly got caught – by of all things, two guys on quad bikes. Well, every day at home I need my wits about me to avoid being run over by the Gaffer on his quad, so these guys were absolutely no match and I quickly lose them.

This seaside really fascinates me and the water – ugh, it tastes of salt and looks disgusting. Quite why anybody needs to put salt on their fish amazes me.

After a while I see the Gaffer carrying a deck chair then a hundred yards on he picks up another two – walks for a few hundred yards and the three of them set the chairs up and settle down on the beach. Why he can't pay for the hire of these chairs like everyone else I really don't know.

The sun is blazing down on his bald head so he uses a handkerchief to cover it, rolls up his trousers to his knees and looks like your typical holiday maker on a picture postcard.

They look a little crowded to me so I know what his next move will be, and sure enough out comes his pipe. He must have doused his tobacco in diesel by the amount of smoke; I notice Tracey and the Missus move upwind of him and everyone downwind leaving the area.

Someone must have noticed how he acquired the deckchairs and alerted the attendant, who tracked him down, demanding money. I'm thinking this may be an interesting conversation. He said he had no money as he was a farmer. 'Will you take plastic?' Asks the Gaffer. 'Yes certainly sir'. Well have my comb, that's plastic. This young guy must have been thinking the minimum wage per hour plus a suntan is never worth the aggro.

'I'll tell you what' says the Gaffer, 'are you a gambling man? If so, I'll give you a good tip'.

'Well yes I do have the occasional flutter', says he. 'Very well then, here's a good tip – don't cross the road if a car is coming or you may get run over'.

I'm thinking this is my chance to relieve the situation so run through this guys legs to distract him. 'Is this your dog sir?', he asks. 'You must be joking', says he, 'I've got a proper sheep dog, not a mongrel like this, who's too small to round up sheep'. I'm thinking to myself you cheeky b....., and with that start body hopping again with this guy chasing me.

They stay on their chairs for a few hours, by which time they are all turning bright red. I'm having a whale of a time avoiding capture. I see up at the far end of the beach donkeys giving rides on the sand. A picture of the Gaffer astride one with the caption 'one silly ass on another' would be quite appropriate.

I see the Gaffer looking in the other direction where there are helicopter rides. One can just see his imagination running wild thinking of a way to invent a double ejector seat for a helicopter and then getting Tony Blair and the Taxman to try it out.

They're on the move, the three of them in the direction of the heli-rides so I tag along at a safe distance. Off the sand at last, so no posse chasing me. The pilot is the spitting image of Biggles – handlebar moustache, whisky drinker's nose and a silk scarf.

'Sorry no dogs allowed on the rides', he says. 'He's my guide dog', pleads the Gaffer. 'I don't see any white stick sir'. 'That's because I only need him for driving'. With that we all climb aboard while Biggles tries to decide if his hearing is playing tricks on him.

The Gaffer has his camera going as soon as we are airborne taking aerial photographs, so that means in a week's time we will be back down here selling them. Biggles turns out to sea which will scupper the photography plans so I stand on the rear seat with my feet on the guy's shoulders and start growling and frothing at the mouth. The old boy asks if he thought I had rabies which made him change course. Back to flying over land again and snap, snap of the camera.

Over the radio we hear, 'Flight HL497 you are violating airspace, please return to your scheduled route'. I start licking Biggles ears which brings the comment from the Gaffer – 'He's just building up to taking a bite out of them, so no sudden movements' In total he took over 50 photographs so should have made a nice profit, if we can sell them on at the right price.

After landing the Missus and Tracey decide they have had enough of the double act between the Gaffer and myself so they head off to the shops and we agree to meet up later. The first thing we both do is to pig out on ice-cream then head off towards the dodgems. I manage to locate one with dual controls so in we both get intent on causing maximum disruption. The buzzer goes and off we all proceed in the same direction at a leisurely pace – out comes his smelly pipe and its like an inner city smog. With that he does a 180 degree turn, I put my pedal to the metal and go as fast as we can into the oncoming vehicles. Well, you've never seen such chaos, two of the attendants chasing us as well as trying to avoid being mown down. When the buzzer goes to end the ride the old boy says the controls are faulty and says he wants his money back or a free ride. They were only too pleased to give him his money back to get rid of the geriatric trouble maker.

The next ride we fancy is the roller coaster but what a queue there is. We join the back of the queue and he whispers in my ear – 'start frothing at the mouth Benny'. He then picks me up and asks the couple in front – 'do you think my dog has rabies' as they hurry away. We keep doing this a dozen or so times and all of a sudden we are right at the front of the queue.

We are on the front two seats, strapped in and away we go. We seem to be climbing for ages until we can see over most of the resort. Then all of a sudden it's down hill, looping the loop, around corners too fast and I'm thinking, that last ice cream was not such a good idea. I'm afraid to look forward so face backwards with my head over the back of the seat, paws over my eyes and then it happened – I threw up over the people behind me. When the ride stopped we had to unload and run to avoid one very angry couple claiming money off us for ruining their clothes and their day out.

It took me half an hour to regain my composure, then it's off we go to the funfair. He spots a coconut shy with a prize of a giant teddy bear so pays for six balls, misses with the first two, then a direct hit, but the coconut did not move.

He missed the next, then another direct hit and still it did not fall. 'Something's wrong here young man - let me see the underside of that coconut'. 'No way sir', he said gruffly. 'Benny, help me out'. With that I leap over the counter and back this guy up to the coconut and sure enough it's tied to the base with string. With that I clamp my teeth firmly around his own coconuts. 'He hasn't been fed today' says the Gaffer. 'OK, sir have the teddy bear, just get your mutt off me'.

The Missus and Tracey are waiting for us. 'Had a good time have you', asks Tracey. 'Not bad, not bad at all' says he. We get home just as the six o'clock news comes on and there is this picture of me caught on video with the newsreader saying – 'Does anyone recognise this dog?' He has caused absolute mayhem today at a beach resort'. Several people were interviewed giving graphic details of how their day had been ruined. The newsreader could hardly keep a straight face. The Gaffer said it was the best day out he had for ages and I could not help but agree with him.

Just had another four cases of Foot and Mouth at Crickhowell which is about 15 miles west of here and 15 miles east of the cases at Brecon three weeks ago. In this latest outbreak stock have been slaughtered off a total of 16 farms.

In neither outbreak does there appear to be any direct contact. The latest theory is that each of these two recent outbreaks are within two miles of the A40 road which was used to transport culled stock to the burial site on the Eppynt Mountain, near Sennybridge back in April and May. But as this was two months ago it seems rather unlikely.

I think I must be getting old by how young the police dogs are looking. I wouldn't advise anyone to grow old, as there's not a lot of future in it.

Anyway I decide to take the Missus to the local park – it's only a 10-minute walk if you run. People are strange aren't they? Some of them sit on the park benches and throw things at the ducks and pigeons. You'd think they would be arrested or get complaints from the RSPB, but they don't and they're quite brazen about it. On a good day it's cakes and biscuits they throw, on a bad day it's stale bread. In fact a quick-minded dog can grab quite generous helpings.

When the Missus stops at the café for a cup of tea I creep off and do some begging. The only people worth begging off are ones with hairs on their clothes, which means they have dogs of their own and will be a soft touch.

Meet up with several of my canine mates who are becoming really stressed because of the restrictions imposed on the countryside because of the Foot and Mouth outbreak. There are so many notices in the park for us dogs to ignore like: 'Don't walk on the grass'. It's OK to run on it, roll on it, dig into it, pee on it – just don't walk on it, OK.

Farmers have just been warned by the Government to embrace change or face financial ruin. The warning has come from new agriculture chief Margaret Beckett who has signalled an end to subsidies. She wants to see a shift away from modern farming methods and more grants to protect the environment and promote rural development, but she did promise that small farmers would not be squeezed out. She gives the impression that the Government understands the problems – the big question is: do they care?

It is inevitable that farming is going to go through a major upheaval and some people will actually be better off if they leave the industry. Farmers are so punch drunk after having suffered setback after setback that they cannot make a clear decision about their future. But the decision will have to be taken, because it will be in their own interests.

These last two weeks has seen some unsettled weather and here at Faulty Farm we have been doing some much needed maintenance work. Repairing holes in the yards with concrete, rebuilding walls that the old boy has driven into and even painting walls of buildings. It makes the place look tidier but does not pay at all.

At one stage I was so engrossed in digging for this flaming rat I had chased into a drain, that I did not notice this constant buzzing sound. Right next to where I was digging was the entrance to a hornet's nest. Big blighters aren't they, and bad tempered. At one stage they were stacked up behind me like planes coming in to land at Heathrow Airport. Exit one dog leaving a rat to live another day.

We have also had the roadside hedges and verges trimmed by 'Big Ron'. A much neater job than some of the guys who trim verges for the local authorities. The Gaffer calls some of their work 'chain harrowing'.

We've also had 'Pete the Feet', our local foot trimmer, in for a day to trim the feet of our cows.

Last night Gareth, Tracey and Moose took me to the Millennium Stadium in Cardiff to see Robbie Williams. Gareth hid me under his coat to get me in, and save paying. Well, what a performer and what a venue. With over 60,000 people there the atmosphere was just electric. I thought the highlight of the show had to be 'She's the One', incidentally written by a Welshman.

More than £100,000 was raised for desperate farmers yesterday as thousands of fun runners joined some of the world's top athletes in a fun run in London. They were contributing to the NFU Supporting Farmers in Crisis Fund. NFU director general Richard McDonald said – 'These are desperate times and every penny raised will be put to the best possible use'. Well done to you all I say.

The RSPCA has warned that Government mismanagement of Foot and Mouth disease could spark another crisis later in the year. It said infection rates could rise again in the Autumn when hill sheep are moved down to farms to mingle with other animals. By the end of this month 100,000 sheep will be being tested for Foot and Mouth each week, a figure expected to rise to 140,000 a week by the Autumn.

The NFU has accused the Government of complacency over a decision to reopen 118,000 miles of rights of way, and promising that the remaining restrictions would be removed within a week.

On Wednesday of last week 10 new outbreaks were confirmed – the highest number in one day for some time.

Tony Blair has ordered an emergency halt to the Foot and Mouth clean up on farms because costs threaten to escalate to an unacceptable £800 million. The PM cracked down when told that contractors carrying out the work were running up bills of £104,000 per farm – or £2 million each day. The cleaning and disinfecting programme is being put on hold until a cheaper means of completing the work has been found. Other EU countries clean up schemes cost only 10 per cent of the amount spent in the UK. In Scotland the average cost has worked out at £30,000 per holding.

So far 8,811 farms have been hit by the epidemic, and 3.6 million animals have been culled. Another 22,000 still await slaughter, and 13,000 carcasses still have to be disposed of. 1.2 million animals have also been culled under the welfare disposal scheme.

The Government has all but brushed the question of a public inquiry aside, even though it is the only way of revealing the truth about the whole sorry affair. Any inquiry would seriously question a policy that has resulted in the deaths of millions of animals, most of which were healthy.

There are other serious questions that must be answered. Crucially, it is now known that a few months before the official start of the epidemic, trials of a new Foot and Mouth vaccine were being carried out in this country. This involved injecting live pigs with vaccine and then artificially infecting them with the Foot and Mouth virus. So somewhere in Britain before it became public knowledge, pigs were incubating the disease. Given that, shortly afterwards, Foot and Mouth broke out in earnest, the question is – did the vaccine trial go horrendously wrong? And is this the real reason why the then Ministry of Agriculture was so opposed to vaccination?

We really do need to know if the epidemic started in mid-February in Northumberland, or is this just a cover up for their own incompetence. In January inquiries were being made about the availability of railway sleepers for pyres. And the whole policy of vaccination, first it was on, then off, then back on and then off again.

There are just too many serious questions that demand answers for this disaster – which is still far from over – to be brushed under the carpet. Indeed, had the Government stamped on Foot and Mouth with the vigour shown in Holland, France and Germany, the outbreak might have been contained within weeks.

The price of a sliced loaf of bread is due to go up by 6p because of the high price of wheat. Milling wheat incidentally is £30 a ton less than four years ago. It's always so easy to blame the farmers isn't it!

Lord Henry Plumb was chairman of the NFU's Animal Health Committee during the 1967 Foot and Mouth epidemic and is now the only surviving member of the Northumberland Committee, which conducted the post epidemic Inquiry. When asked which of the recommendations had successive Government's most culpably failed to implement, he replied: 'Oh, that's easy, by ignoring our recommendations on meat imports they left the door wide open for the disease to return. We warned them, either you control imports, or you will eventually have to move to a vaccination policy, it's as simple as that'.

Modulation: what is it? It is the siphoning off of a percentage of direct payments to farmers to fund rural development measures. Starting from 2001 it will be 2.5 per cent and rising to 4.5 per cent by 2005. It will be deducted from the sheep annual Premium, Beef Special Premium, Suckler Cow Premium, Slaughter Premium, Extensification Premium, Arable Area Payments, Hops and Seeds. We have just received our first payment for the Sheep Annual Premium Scheme and 2.5 per cent had been deducted.

It is expected that the majority of the money from modulation will be spent within a year of it being made available. The money will be spent on Processing and Marketing Grants, Organic Farming Scheme, plus additional money for Woodland Grant Schemes linked to environmental agreements. The Government giveth and the Government taketh away.

It has now been disclosed that compensation cheques paid to farmers affected by F&M has not come from our own Government but from the EU Livestock Reduction Fund whose aim is to reduce the total number of livestock in the EU Countries. It appears that the only contribution our own Government is making is for cleaning and disinfecting and now they are trying to economise on that aspect.

This last week of July has seen temperatures into the eighties with some superb haymaking weather. We have a fairly large acreage to make off other people's land so keep the mower going for three days non-stop and within a week it is all baled up.

The potatoes which only a month ago were struggling now look quite good, and we have started lifting on a small scale.

Sheep on the Brecon Beacons which have been tested for F&M anti-bodies have shown an unacceptably high level, so 4,000 have been slaughtered, with testing still being carried out in the area. The old boy was born and brought up in the Libanus area of Powys so knows many of the farms and farmers affected. His brother still farms at the home farm but so far has not had his stock culled.

The Army is to help slaughter up to 2 million sheep in a massive cull that has been ordered as there is no market for these light hill lambs due to the export ban imposed in the wake of F&M. Several of our major supermarkets have announced their own promotions for these light lambs but not until the knock-down price of £10 a head was announced, which means they can buy them for no more than this figure.

It seems crazy that we continue to import meat from countries with F&M disease for our own military and health service canteens and then bury our own meat in pits.

The last Sunday of July and it's a very early start as Tracey, Moose, Sandra, Carl, Jake and myself are off to Bedfordshire to the Country Landowners Association (CLA) Game Fair. That snooty Jake and I have to share the space in the rear of the old boy's estate car, and as he is quite large it does not leave much room for me. He also says I have fleas which he does not want to inherit. The journey takes nearly three hours so we get there at about 9 o'clock to scorching hot temperatures.

Jake and I have our usual pep talk – 'Jake behave yourself'. 'Benny no dog fights, and don't go off ratting, but of course there won't be any rats here', says Tracey. It's the first time I've been to a show like this and just cannot believe how much is happening.

We look in on the ferret racing and I'm thinking these things look too much like a mink to be a friend of mine. Birds of Prey. Now these are quite fascinating and large too, some of them, big enough to carry a dog of my size, so I stay fairly close to Tracey.

In the distance we see a 4x4 course and I'm thinking, this is more up our street but this instructor guy who's trained in the art of hi-tech bullshit goes around with you trying to impress you with the merits of the vehicle he's hoping you will buy. We decide to give that one a miss but will come back by later and try for an unaccompanied burn-up through the course.

Further along is a dog racing course, a scurry I believe they call it, made up of a course about 60 metres in length with a wall of straw bales either side and the dog with the fastest time is the winner. Jake and I are running alongside each other and Tracey and Sandra are at the far end shouting encouragement. The bell goes and Jake is off like a rocket leaving me a long way behind. He is nearly at the end of the course when I am only halfway, when all of a sudden – a divine fragrance, I drop anchor, engage four-wheel braking and screech to a halt checking from where this fragrance is emanating.

Yes, you've guessed it, I've smelt a rat! Left-hand side of the track, second layer of bales – I can even see the end of his tail. Make a grab, miss his tail, he breaks cover and it's across the site we go. Big rat, in good condition by the speed he runs at, me in hot pursuit, Tracey shouting at me to let him go – well! The very thought of it.

The Gaffer and Missus were at home watching 'Countryfile', before the week's weather forecast, and actually saw me on the box. John Craven was interviewing Patrick Bosanquet, CLA President, live on telly and they see this rat being pursued by me in the background but I did not have time to wave.

By this time I have a pack of other dogs (mostly terriers) following me in pursuit of this flaming rat. Roland starting to panic now so nips into a tent selling country clothing where people are shopping and the screams of terror on seeing this rat - well what a load of fairies. Out the back of the tent and towards a large tree and I'm thinking he's going to do the same trick as a squirrel and climb the tree, but no, at the base of the tree is a small hole and he disappears down there, to live to tell the tale.

When we get to a stand selling dog accessories I start scratching myself and Tracey buys me a flea collar. I can't stand wearing a collar but it is preferable to having a load of passengers in this hot weather.

Tracey is really into the golfing and as there is a good quality course almost adjoining us, the two of us spend a fair bit of time there practising for an impending tournament. My task is finding lost balls and as we get paid so much for each one I find, it almost covers her annual subscription.

The day of the match arrives, a very good turn out and weather dry, but heavy showers forecast. The person who Tracey is drawn to play against has the audacity to say that I should not be on the course. However, after consulting with Wyndham the Golf I have the OK but I'm thinking to myself, it's my turn next young lady.

The game gets under way and it soon becomes apparent that her ladyship is a very accomplished player. I'm thinking my best plan of attack is to pretend to look for lost balls while awaiting my chance to level the score. By the fourth tee she is leading by two shots but slices her long drive up the fairway to land less than one metre from the rough. As Tracey is taking her shot I dart out of the undergrowth and move the ball back two metres behind a tree. Nobody suspected anything but her language was less than ladylike. She lost two strokes on the fourth to put them level.

A very close fought match and by the time we get to the end of the game it's Her Ladyship winning by two strokes, just as the heavens open and everyone makes a dash for the shelter of an old storage building. Golf bags are thrown on the floor and when nobody is looking, I find a spare club and slip it into her bag.

By the time we get back to the clubhouse I've told Tracey about the extra club so she summons Wyndham the Golf and sure enough there are 15 clubs in her bag rather than the maximum permitted of 14. This means she has two points added to her score which means she is level with Tracey. Several other players in the tournament have better scores but it's the taking part that matters, not the winning.

One of my favourite sports of all time has to be quad bike racing. Due to the Foot and Mouth epidemic, several meetings have been cancelled this year, but we find one on the Cotswolds in an arable area that is still going ahead. A very thorough cleaning and disinfecting of the Land Rover and trailer and the bike and it's off the Gaffer, Tracey and I go for a great day out.

There are three classes – one for girls, one for Young Farmers and one for older competitors. Four bikes race at a time and the winner from each heat takes part in the finals. One of the conditions is that a bona-fide sheep or cattle dog must accompany the rider. Tracey is drawn in the first heat and I am hanging on behind – if the dog falls off you are automatically disqualified. We win our heat so qualify for the final, but did no good in it.

The next race is the Young Farmers, and boy, can some of these guys get a wiggle on – it was some of the best racing I have ever seen.

The last race is for the more mature farmers and we are drawn in the second heat. The Gaffer is nuts when he is on his quad but we only won by half a length which qualifies us for the finals. When we are waiting for the other heats he gets out his hip flask and pours most of the contents into the fuel tank. 'Methanol Benny, so hold tight' he says.

As we line up for the final I notice our bike is smoking more than normal and we do a wheely as the flag comes down. Straight into the lead we go with clouds of smoke billowing out of the exhaust. Across the set-aside field, through the woods, the stream, up the hill and towards the finishing line, with a 50 yard lead over Popeye in second place, to take the chequered flag.

Popeye goes across to an official to make a complaint. Over to us they come. 'Did you put something into your tank out of your hip flask sir?' 'Certainly not', says the Gaffer, taking out his hip flask and drinking the remains to allay their fears. 'Just my normal tipple sir.' They seem satisfied and award us first prize. I hope the old boy does not light his pipe for a few hours or we will all be blown to pieces.

Popeye is still convinced he should have won and went away muttering to himself. I can't stand a bad loser, can you? The Gaffer says it doesn't matter if you win or lose – it's where you lay the blame that counts.

More than 1,000 miles of footpaths, closed five months ago due to the Foot and Mouth epidemic, have reopened. Restrictions on almost 65 per cent of footpaths in the Lake District and Cumbria are lifted. A council leader said, 'A balance has to be struck between helping the tourist industry while doing what we can to protect our livestock'.

Teams of meat inspectors are having to check all over-30 months cattle to make sure they are fit for human consumption even though they are being incinerated and will never be eaten. This is an EU ruling that is considerably slowing down the whole process of slaughtering these older, unproductive stock that are eating into next winter's forage supplies.

In 1993 farmers were getting 219 pence per kilo for lamb that was being sold at 375 pence – a profit margin of 156 pence. Today the same quality lamb fetches just 155 pence while the retail price is 555 pence – a difference of £4 a kilo. Farmers are receiving less than £30 for animals that would cost, in joint form, more than £100 on the supermarket shelf.

The three fields of Spring barley that were undersown have just been mowed ready for wholecrop silage. About one-third of the acreage had lodged fairly badly so rather than leave too much waste by cutting with a Kemper header on a self propelled machine, we mowed it off ourselves. To reduce the wastage of grains we unbolted and removed the conditioner unit off the mower, and then by reducing the Power Take-Off (PTO) revs we had negligible losses.

The crop was about three weeks away from being fit to combine, so we were one week too early cutting, but due to the lodging we were concerned about the damage to the undersown grass. The day after cutting it was rowed up and the following day it was picked up by a flywheel chop forage harvester which did an excellent job. The kit belonged to a relation of the Gaffer called 'Kev the Rev', and he certainly lived up to his name. One good day and the job was completed in good time and the pit rolled and sheeted with what should be some fairly good quality feed for the cows next Winter, and more importantly enough of it. Most farmers have completed their second silage cuts this last week with surprisingly heavy cuts of good quality material.

We are now supplying several shops and chip shops with potatoes so are lifting, grading and delivering most days. The spud harvester 'did the splits' one day. A bracket on part of the steering mechanism broke off and we could not move. A phone call to 'Eric Bald Eagle', the machinery doctor soon had him arrive with his mobile welder in the middle of the field, and in a very short time we were working once more.

Pressure is now growing for a public inquiry into the Foot and Mouth epidemic, as this would be the only way the Government can regain the trust lost over the handling of the epidemic.

With the Government running scared they are now putting the blame onto farmers and clean-up contractors. Thirty-seven farmers have had pay-outs of over one million pounds each, which they are portraying as wrong. If their stock is worth that amount and it is the fault of the Government that the disease is still not under control after five months, then why blame the farmers.

Cleaning and disinfecting, which was suspended for 10 days, has now been reviewed and is continuing.

Last year the net value of all farm produce was £1.9 billion. By contrast Foot and Mouth has so far cost taxpayers £2.2 billion in direct costs, and several times that in indirect costs such as damage to tourism. So far Labour has remained largely unscathed by the crisis, but there is evidence that taxpayers are becoming increasingly resentful at seeing so much money being poured into a single industry.

Elliot Morley, the Minister who is responsible for animal heath, said the Government would meet its obligations to farmers by paying compensation for the remainder of this outbreak – but emphasised that it would be 'the last time' they could expect such payments.

The new boss of DEFRA, Margaret Beckett, has taken her full five weeks of holiday entitlement in the middle of the biggest crisis the British countryside has ever experienced. It would have looked better if she had taken some of her holidays now and some at a later date. Do they really know what is happening in the countryside? YES. Do they really care what is happening? I'll leave you to answer that one.

Many politicians are blaming the spread of the epidemic on the early refusal of the NFU to co-operate with a vaccination programme. They say 'the NFU seems to think the public purse is to be dipped into whenever it wants – there is no other industry that receives these kinds of subsidies'. Experts say that by opting for a quick cull policy, instead of following a programme of selected vaccination, the Government had increased the total cost of the foot and mouth epidemic from between £1.5 billion and £2 billion to about £5 billion by the end of the year. These figures took into account the cost of the clean-up campaign, compensating farmers and the loss from tourism. This has not deterred the Government from its stated position of leaving vaccination as an option, but one which it has yet to implement, a policy endorsed by the NFU which says that vaccination would irredeemably damage the export market.

The Government's patience for farmers has run dry – farming will never be the same again.

The mass cull of sheep on the Brecon Beacons continues after foot and mouth anti-bodies are still being found in tested sheep. So far 6,500 have been slaughtered and results on a further 3,000 are still awaited. All the evidence so far suggests the disease has been spreading on the mountain from one original point and that the level of infection drops sharply as we move out from that point, and test adjacent groups of sheep. Some graziers are mounting a legal challenge to the cull decision.

In North Yorkshire up to 50,000 sheep are being tested on farms around Thirsk. Officials are desperate to prevent the disease spreading into the pig population. More than 8,600 pigs have already been slaughtered as a precaution. Devon, Cornwall and Somerset are now officially infection free from Foot and Mouth. Devon was originally one of the most heavily infected areas.

Government officials meet farmers leaders this week to discuss a possible autumn resumption of livestock markets in counties of Britain that are free of the disease. They seem to think that this could happen as early as mid-September.

On the first Sunday of August we always have a cricket match between our village and the adjoining village. None of the players can belong to a cricket team, so the level of play leaves rather a lot to be desired but there certainly is no lack of enthusiasm.

Gareth has been selected to play as have several of his Young Farmer mates and the Gaffer, Missus and myself go along for moral support. As we pull into the car park, this open top sports job rolls up, being driven by a Leonardo

Decaprio lookalike with a smile that would melt knicker elastic at 50 paces. His name apparently is James Ponsonby Eyebrows and his old man owns the cricket pitch and also most of the parish.

This cricket game is completely new to me so I had looked up its meaning in the dictionary – a leaping insect noted for the chirping sounds of the male (no that must be the other cricket) but as the game progressed, and more beer was drunk there were some strange sounds being made on the pitch.

We settled down to watch this fascinating game with my new mate James sitting alongside us. He must have been vaccinated with a gramophone needle when he was younger as he did not stop talking. 'Clear spot at silly mid on', 'move a fielder to silly mid off', leg before, wide, bye – the Gaffer was looking at him wondering if he was on the 'wacky baccy'.

With that I see the ball from one of the opposition batsmen heading straight towards us and a certain boundary score. Quick as flash I make my move and catch the ball a metre before the line and run as fast as I can with the ball in my mouth and throw it at the three trees planted in the middle of this level field to run the guy out. Much discussion about the extra player but as one of our team had been injured it was decided I should take his place.

I notice further down the field are another three small trees where the other batsman hovers and all of a sudden the sight of all these trees with odd shaped pieces of wood across the top of them remind me that I am on my second can of coke and will soon want to go.

By some stroke of luck we manage to bowl them all out for only 80 runs. These cricket balls are damn hard aren't they – I have to be careful not to break my teeth when I catch it.

Gareth's team comes in to bat but within an hour we have a torrential storm of rain which means the end of play for the day. We all adjourn to the pavilion and eat loads of cucumber sandwiches and home made cakes. Everyone else is on the beer but I decide to stick with the coke.

Lord Haskins, the Labour peer appointed by Tony Blair to rescue areas hit by foot and mouth, backs a policy of vaccination of infected animals and paints a bleak picture of the future of farming. He predicts that half the current 240,000 farms will disappear in the next 20 years, and says that farmers had been mollycoddled for too long. He is also calling for a massive shake up of farm subsidies.

The Government has a duty to protect this country from imports of infected produce, in which it failed. If it fails again it should still be held liable.

The outraged but well fed urban population demand to know which other industries receives such generous compensation. Answer: all of them. There is not a single industry in this country which, if the Government decreed that its assets must be destroyed, would not be reimbursed in full.

Bear in mind that farmers are not being compensated for loss of income but merely for loss of their assets. Imagine a shopkeeper having all his stock taken from his shelves and destroyed by order of the Government, then he too would be compensated for destruction of these goods.

The debate about vaccination keeps rambling on but this policy is not as simple as it seems.

The Dutch had vaccinated in a ring around their few cases – then have to slaughter all these vaccinated animals at a later date. However, the spread of the disease in Holland was very quickly halted. The only country to have tried mass-vaccination of sheep was Uruguay – which had eventually given up.

This Government that suspended cleaning and disinfecting of farms for 10 days is the same one that has been willing to wave blank cheques at the Millennium Dome. The Dome project is still costing the taxpayer almost as much per week as the cost of disinfecting affected farms, yet they appear to be willing to bankroll the Dome project indefinitely.

There have been two great mysteries to the Foot and Mouth crisis. The first is why the Government's response has been so incompetent. Everything it has done has been designed, not to bring the disease to a rapid end, but to kill as many livestock as possible and inflict maximum damage on Britain's small livestock farmers.

The second mystery is why the Government's propaganda machine has been so consistent in its efforts to blacken the farmers and, where possible, to blame them as the real cause of the problem.

One in 10 of all farm animals in the UK has already been destroyed. If the epidemic continues well into next year, as now seems very likely, this number could be as high as one in five. Tens of thousands of small livestock producers are becoming so traumatised that they will be getting out of farming forever.

More than 9,000 farms have so far been cleared of livestock due to the foot and mouth crisis, with more than 3.7 million animals slaughtered and nearly 1.5 million slaughtered under the welfare scheme.

It has now emerged that the EU is paying 60 per cent of the costs of compensation and cleaning and disinfecting of premises and not 100 per cent as was being reported just a few weeks ago. However, teams of EU Audit Investigators who are visiting the UK looking into claims of Government mishandling of the crisis, and claims of fraud, are forcing the Government to apportion the blame to, of all people, the farmers. This then seems to be the cause of all the farmer bashing in recent weeks. The Government's spin machine always manages to divert the blame.

Our pedigree ewes are five miles away and the two senior stock rams are here at home. We have to get the vet to inspect all the stock here at home and supply us with a movement licence to take Adam up to the ewes. Jim will be joining him in about a month's time. We should now start lambing just after the New Year which will give us time to clean the sheds out after the turkeys.

The weather is quite humid and showery this week so it is ideal for 'grubs' in the sheep (these modern sprays and pour-ons are a waste of time compared to the dips we used years ago).

A very rigorous blight spraying programme is being adhered to – so far we have sprayed five times with the sixth imminent. We are now lifting potatoes on an almost daily basis and try if possible not to lift when the haulm is wet to avoid the spread of blight to the tubers once they have been bagged.

Foot and Mouth, BSE, floods and low supermarket prices have failed to put people off wanting to buy farmland. Last year 22 per cent of farms sold were purchased by people with no experience of owning a farm or farming land, so it seems the lure of owning land is as strong as ever.

Did you know the most accident-prone dog is a chocolate Labrador, with over half requiring veterinary treatment at some time in their life? Britain's 10.4 million dog owners spend about £124 million on pet insurance each year, with one in three claiming on their policies. They make an average of two trips to the vet each year, spending £115.

The 10th August and the Government has announced there will be no full scale inquiry into the Foot and Mouth crisis. So it seems that crucial evidence of mishandling the crisis is unlikely to be made public.

There will be three independent inquiries which will examine the Government's handling of the crisis, the scientific issues surrounding the outbreak and the future of farming. The Lib-Dems say: 'It is outrageous the government intends to investigate itself in secret. This is all too reminiscent of the Tory government's refusal to set up a public enquiry into BSE'.

Compassion in World Farming has warned that up to eight million animals will be culled by next April unless a vaccination policy is adopted. The pressure group says the disease must be brought under control before Winter or it will regain its grip on the countryside in the colder weather.

The question of vaccination rather than slaughter has been raised by ministers. But their claims that there were sufficient quantities of vaccine of the correct strain and potency have no more credibility than the officials that have made such a hash of the slaughter policy.

Foot and Mouth has claimed its most expensive victim. The Government has paid out £50,000 compensation for a single sheep. A pedigree Swaledale breeding ram called Mossdale Nuggett was culled after foot and mouth broke out around Settle and Kirkby Lonsdale in Northern England.

Nuggett was a Swaledale ram – a breed known for is high quality wool, its hardiness and its ability to survive on the Cumbrian Hills. He was jointly owned by two farmers in the region, and was bought at auction in 1997 for £50,000 and was the highest price ever recorded for the breed.

Lord Haskins, the Labour peer responsible for farming recovery is quoted as saying, 'Farms will get bigger and that's a good thing. A lot of agriculture reformers, like the Prince of Wales want farmers to stand around being subsidised and making thatched roofs. Well, that's for the birds'. He says that 'The people who have come out of the present crisis best of all have been the ones who have actually had foot and mouth. They have lost their assets but they have got the interest on the money until they restock. The people who have been most affected are farmers in the restricted areas who haven't had foot and mouth and also cannot move their livestock'.

Elliot Morley, the Agriculture Minister with responsibility for animal health, has said that farmers are 'a pretty ungrateful lot'.

David Handley, leader of the protest group, Farmers for Action, called the minister's comments an 'insult'. He said 'If Mr Morley wants to describe farmers as ungrateful then let him, but at least we are up-front about our position, which is more than I can say for him. We don't expect to be propped up or subsidised or cushioned but we do expect a level playing field, so we can show the rest of the world what we can do'.

Have just had a day with the Gaffer spraying spuds for blight – I think this must be the sixth application this year. The spuds look remarkably well, as does everyone else's, and it seems inevitable that the price will drop. However, we did see an encouraging sign today that the price is still fairly high – someone had been helping themselves to some in a field adjoining a road. The Gaffer says that nobody pinches them when they are only a quid a bag.

Near six months after the start of the Foot and Mouth outbreak, the Government has been accused of complete inactivity over improved measures to halt illegal meat imports into the country. This is despite repeated warnings to both DEFRA and Customs and Excise by farmers' leaders.

Experts complained that a disease time bomb was waiting to go off at any of Britain's airports, and they believe the volume of illegal meat entering the UK from Africa leaves little doubt organised gangs are behind the operation. In the month of February alone 5½ tons of illegal meat from Lagos, some of it dripping with blood, plus other packed meats of bush rats, antelope meat, fish and monkeys were confiscated.

Customs and Excise seem more concerned with apprehending smugglers of alcohol and tobacco than illegal meat supplies. They claim they do not have the staff to tackle the sources of these imports.

This unsatisfactory situation cannot be allowed to continue. Lord Haskins has suggested farmers could alleviate their financial problems by getting a second job. He said, 'I can see people milking their cows in the morning, working on a car assembly line during the day, then milking their cows in the evening. This is the sort of pattern I think is going to grow'.

Several new cases of Foot and Mouth are still being confirmed every day. A dozen farms in the Abergavenny, Crickhowell area have been directly affected, with many more affected by contiguous cull procedures.

The cull of hefted sheep is continuing within the Brecon Beacons National Park. A total of 2,000 were rounded up for slaughter on Saturday (11th August) with a further 6,000 to follow. Some of these hefted sheep have not been blood tested, but are being culled as a 'fire-break' exercise to stop the spread of the disease.

I nearly had a serious accident last night when I was with Gareth in the Land Rover getting the cows in to milk. I normally ride in the vehicle to the furthest field and then get out to drive the cows in. Anyway it was tipping down with rain so I stayed in the cab barking at them out of the window. However, as I was stretched out too far, and the vehicle hit a bump I actually fell out, but luckily avoided being run over. The worst part was that it was in a very muddy gateway and I got absolutely filthy. The lad did hose me down afterwards but it was still an experience I could have done without.

Went with the Gaffer and his mate 'Ray JCB' to an evening machinery sale near Ross-on-Wye. As it was one of the few sales to have been held this year, there was an enormous crowd present, which gave one an opportunity to meet up with some mates that one had not seen for ages.

The Gaffer ended up buying a potato harvester so was straight on the phone to Gareth, who had milked early, to get down there with a tractor to pick it up. The harvester was the same make as the one we have but had a picking-off table at the back, so in certain conditions when we are bulking in the Autumn, it will be simpler to pick off the back of the harvester than to put them over the cleaner/hopper in the building, with hopefully less damage. It will also mean we can fill boxes in the field if we need to by driving alongside the harvester.

Farmers from across the country are planning to descend on London and voice their anger at being denied a public inquiry into the Foot and Mouth epidemic. Militant farmers have pledged to bring the country to its knees if Tony Blair then refuses to listen to their calls. Campaign groups from across the country are to call themselves the Foot and Mouth Disease Alliance.

Lord Haskins said yesterday, 'We have got a lot of lessons to learn from the French. I wish we could get our farmers to be more enterprising and a little bit less reliant on the state when things go wrong'. I think he should have chosen his words more wisely in this case as French farmers are always protesting and blocking major ports and cities. His words may come back to haunt him in the next few months.

We have just started selling our yearling rams for breeding. Our problem is that we are under an E Notice so we can only sell to farms that are in the same category or a 'dirtier' category to ourselves. This leaves us with a much reduced number of buyers but so far it is going better than expected.

More cases of Foot and Mouth have been confirmed in Wales over the past week as the slaughter toll of hefted sheep on the Brecon Beacons has now topped 20,000 and blood testing of a further 30,000 is under way. There are a total of upwards of 100,000 sheep grazing the Beacons and the pro-vaccination National Foot and Mouth Group believes that without a change in policy, the whole area could soon be cleared of stock.

Heard a good quote today – any farmer who has not got an overdraft is either a damn liar or is not trying very hard.

Compassion for World Farming continues to support a vaccination policy as a means of stamping out Foot and Mouth disease. It says that in the past seven weeks, more than 6,000 animals have been slaughtered each day.

The question of the UK's involvement with Europe continues to be a topic of debate. As with most issues there are arguments for and against whichever view you favour. I am aware of the sovereignty issue but basically I am pro-Europe. My reason is that whichever Government is in power in the UK, they will not look after its farmers as they do in continental Europe.

These past few months, as F&M has savaged farming and the countryside, has highlighted the indifference the present Government has towards agriculture. UK agriculture is only 2 per cent of GDP, and with less than 2 per cent of the population involved in it.

The Government has never had the disease under control. They are afraid to hold a public inquiry, as they know all too well that the outcome would be embarrassing to them. In recent weeks with spin and leaks, we have been subjected to gutter politics.

Why say it is costing over £100,000 to disinfect farms when it is actually costing less than half that figure? And who has been in control of the clean-up anyway? Not farmers but DEFRA officials, so they should be getting the blame.

The high levels of livestock valuations have been questioned but it was DEFRA who agreed to the figures.

In my opinion, the Government has stooped to a new unacceptable level of politics, this includes Tony Blair who took control of the disease when he wanted a clear run to hold the election – 12 months before it had to be held. DEFRA minister Margaret Beckett has irresponsibly taken five weeks' holiday in the midst of the epidemic.

In the months of August, September and October over 3 million animal movements take place as store cattle and suckled calves are sold. This is a crucial phase and a decision from vets on what animals can be shifted is needed urgently.

Rough estimates suggest about 800,000 stores and calves are caught on their farm of birth. With forage running short and accommodation becoming tight, fears of another welfare crisis is rising. Many livestock farms have limited accommodation, no cereals and no straw.

The 20-day standstill further inhibits movements, as a finisher with one holding will only realistically be able to make two purchases during September and October. Some people are suggesting if you can't move the animals to the forage, then move the forage to the animals, but that won't work if you have no accommodation.

We've got Big Ron back in hedge trimming which for us canines must be the worst farm operation of the whole year – you just cannot believe the number of thorns that I get in my feet. The sooner they put deflectors and perhaps fans to blow the trimmings back into the hedge the better. The cows also complain about the grief it causes them.

Jim has now been taken to some away land to help Adam get the pedigree ewes in lamb, so at least I do not have to put up with his moaning.

The Gaffer won a prize of a ride in a hot air balloon some time ago and now that restrictions have been partly lifted in certain areas, he's been invited along for his free ride. The Missus takes us to the departure point and I was expecting to be left behind, but the old boy said I could go along if I could manage to get into the basket unnoticed.

It really is quite a complicated procedure to blow the balloon up. It is set on its side and air is blown in, then one burner is lit, more air, then another burner and so on until all four burners are lit and the balloon is upright. During all this procedure I manage to sneak into the basket unobserved, except by the Gaffer.

There are two guys in charge of the balloon and 10 others. I thought the old boy had a big gut on him but there was this American guy who must have weighed 25 stone who just kept on about how much bigger and better things were in the States. I'm thinking to myself if they are that good whatever are you doing over here mate?

The ropes are released and it's up we go at a surprisingly fast rate. I'm still hiding in a corner of the basket and inadvertently rub against Motor Mouth who lets out a yell – 'There's a damn racoon in this airship, I'll throw the damn thing out'. 'You can't do that', chorus a few other passengers, 'anyway it's a dog not a racoon'.

'We don't normally allow animals on board', says the boss man, 'but he'll have to stay. Anyway whose dog is it?' Nobody answered so the Gaffer says it belongs to the people from where we took off and he said he would look after me and return me home – the lying so-and-so. Everyone else thought he was a damn hero.

The old boy picked me up so that I could see over the side of the basket – oh my gawd, we must be 600 feet in the air and I can see pheasants and rabbits running down the tramlines in the corn. It really is quite fascinating looking down on the houses and countryside but I do not really have a very good head for heights and already I'm wishing I'd not had that last can of coke before take off.

'Are you sure that four-legged creature is not a racoon, as the damn thing stinks like one', says Fat Belly. The Gaffer whispers in my ear – 'We'll have to nobble this big fat bugger before we land Benny – got any ideas?'

'Can't this contraption go any faster', says New York Ted, 'I could walk faster, and I'm starting to get hungry'. I'm quietly thinking to myself you've had more meals than meal times by your figure anyway. Everyone else on the trip was really great, the old boy was even cracking a few jokes but Abraham Lincoln just kept on bellyaching the whole trip. 'It's a good job I brought some food along', he says as he opens this holdall to expose an absolute mountain of grub.

'There's a landing place over there', says Captain Kirk, 'quickly, lose some height'. Not too quickly if you don't mind, I've just left my stomach 300 feet above us. A jolt as we land and the flap is opened to let the air out and the basket nearly tips on its side. With that I feel an overwhelming desire to throw up and notice Fat Belly's holdall open and throw up all over his stash of food, and quickly close the bag to hide the evidence.

Out of the basket we all climb and start to help to fold up the balloon to load onto the recovery vehicle that has been trailing us, along with a mini-bus to take us back to the starting point.

'That's a mighty fine 4x4 you have as a recovery vehicle, do you mind if I ride with you?' says Bill Clinton. 'Not at all', says the driver not really realising what he is letting himself in for.

The rest of us pile into the mini-bus and two miles down the road the recovery vehicle is stopped and Big Mac is pouring the contents of his holdall out onto the verge which really amused Captain Kirk who had witnessed the little incident on landing.

'Well done racoon', he said, 'every dog has his day'.

What's the definition of a farm? A piece of land surrounded by red tape – and it's the red tape we'd like to get rid of.

US President George W. Bush this week signed off another emergency aid package for his country's beleaguered farmers – the fourth such bail out in as many years. The latest deal will see about £3.9 billion being paid to growers to help them through another serious drought. Grain and cotton producers will get the bulk of the payments with the remainder going to oilseed growers. The latest payout means that the US has spent over £21 billion in four years in emergency farm aid.

EU officials have been dismayed by the US action saying that total taxpayer funding to agriculture now runs at £54 billion a year, compared to £39 billion in the EU. Yet the US only has 2 million farmers compared to 7 million in the EU.

It seems that US emergency packages have now become so routine that farmers are basing their planting decisions on them.

US parliamentarians are now starting to negotiate a new long term farm Bill, to come into effect next year to replace the 1996 Freedom to Farm Act, which sought to reduce US taxpayer support for the industry, but failed to do so.

Six months ago today the first case of Foot and Mouth was confirmed at an abattoir near Brentwood in Essex. The total now stands at 1,960 cases, the rural economy is in crisis and the Government still won't listen to demands for a full public inquiry.

For months the Government has been trying to convince the public that the crisis is almost over, but the people are not fooled. New cases are being confirmed daily with two cases yesterday in Cumbria and North Yorkshire.

The total number of animals slaughtered in the UK as a result of the crisis has risen to 3,750,000, with another 20,000 awaiting slaughter, and 1,420,000 slaughtered on welfare grounds.

It is time Prime Minister Tony Blair and his Government started listening to the people who elected them. There are still many questions demanding answers: Where did the disease come from? Why has it taken so long to begin to get to grips with it? Why did the Government drag its feet in the early days? Why were the lessons of the 1967 outbreak not learned and put into practice?

The big issue is that the front door that allowed the disease into the country in the first place is still wide open, six months later. We are still importing a lot of meat from foreign countries where the disease is endemic and this needs to be resolved immediately.

A mid-Wales teacher vowed to fight on yesterday after the High Court rejected her bid to halt the cull of healthy animals in the Brecon Beacons. She must now pay legal costs, which may be as high as £25,000.

The county of Devon is to hold its own public inquiry into the Foot and Mouth epidemic. There were 173 confirmed cases in the county and the inquiry will be held with the people's participation, in partnership with the County Council.

The Foot and Mouth Alliance yesterday held a march in London to 10 Downing Street to hand in a petition signed by 30,000 people demanding a full, open and public inquiry into the handling of the epidemic.

One batch of rams we sold has gone to a farm within 10 km of an outbreak. This meant a risk assessment being carried out here and at the purchaser's farm by a Ministry vet. The purchaser then had to have his cattle trailer washed and disinfected at an approved centre and then sealed with a special Ministry number. When he arrived here another Ministry vet was present to inspect the sheep and break the seal on the stock trailer. It all sounds very complicated but in all fairness DEFRA staff and officials were extremely helpful and the whole process took only four or five days.

At last the weather has taken up and we have started combining Spring barley. The yields are nothing very exciting but considering it is only about 15 weeks since it was planted we are pleasantly surprised. The moisture is down to 16 per cent with an excellent crop of straw which is stacked inside the buildings housing the turkeys, which will be arriving shortly.

The combine is one of my favourite machines to ride in because I can see right down into the crop and check out the wildlife. Not only that but the cab is air-conditioned which is just brilliant on a scorching hot day. Some of the wheat straw is stacked on top of the silage pit, some around the walls of the potato sheds and the rest is sold.

We have sold another batch of Pedigree Yearling rams to a local farmer. The guys who have bought them have also bought a consignment of ewes so they are hoping to move the rams and the ewes on the same day partly to reduce the effects of the 20 day standstill restrictions imposed, or else they could not sell any stock (except for slaughter) for 21 days.

Ewan Cameron, chairman of the Countryside Agency, has called for vaccine trials to contain Foot and Mouth hot-spots and protect flocks of hill sheep. He has said the public would not tolerate another mass cull of animals to control any future epidemic. The Countryside Agency has just launched a report putting the cost of the epidemic to farming, tourism and the service sector as high as £8.8 billion.

With the restrictions imposed due to F&M disease and public footpaths closed, life is not really a bowl of cherries anymore. We see less of our friends and neighbours and do not visit ourselves unless it is absolutely essential.

Anyway today Tracey and I have decided to go for a long walk but taking care to avoid passing any fields with livestock in them. The weather looks promising as we leave Faulty Farm and across our own fields to the motorway. The noise from these concrete-surfaced roads is absolutely deafening to us canines. We used Brocks Lane (badger underpass) to get to the other side. I'm not too partial to badgers and still have the scars to prove it. They live largely on earthworms and have this disgusting habit of uncovering dried out cow dung pats to find them.

We continue along a very quiet lane and pass a dairy farm on our right-hand side run by two elderly brothers. The Gaffer says the farm has never had a shovelful of lime applied in 40 years, so I can only assume they must be tenants and are hoping one day to buy the farm for next to nothing.

Because of restrictions on walkers there seems to be far more wildlife than in previous years. We cross some arable land known as Castle View, and back onto the main road and alongside a dairy farm that always seems to have more cows than grass to feed them. They have a rake of a dog that I cannot quite make out, who spends most of the day riding around in a pick-up and most of the night roaming around the village.

Alongside a river and fields of cereals and potatoes known as Sleepy Hollow. Tracey and I stop for a picnic lunch and I hear sounds of a teenage couple participating in immoral nocturnal practices. On further investigation I observe them in a wooded clearing and it is all so embarrassing. I have to close one eye to avoid seeing too much. I quickly make my way back to Tracey who has observed a family of otters playing on the bank of the river.

We continue on up a long steep hill called Sugar Loaf View before coming to Handyship Down and fields full of Jersey cows grazing contentedly. All along the lanes are smells of wild animals that have crossed over last night – squirrels, rabbits, weasels and the occasional rat – this is when my sense of keeping up with Tracey completely leaves me and I cannot help but try to catch the things.

Any fields of corn that have partly lodged have hordes of young crows feeding on the grain.

These hard roads play hell with my feet, so we take another break and watch buzzards soaring high in the air, looking for prey to swoop down on.

Down Greenfly Hill with its mass of converted barns which used to be a bustling stock farm. Over Willow Brook and alongside a very neat dairy farm called Hoppyville Hollow, with its freshly-painted walls and manicured gardens.

By now my feet are absolutely killing me so Tracey gets on the phone for the Missus to come and pick us up and take us back to Faulty Farm.

Already we are two-thirds of the way through what must be the most traumatic year livestock farmers have ever faced. There have now been 2,000 cases of foot and mouth since the disease was first confirmed in February.

The outbreak in the Brecon Beacons seems to be being brought under control by means of a firebreak cull with no new confirmed cases for nearly a month, but testing is still continuing for the presence of antibodies.

What is very worrying is the number of cases in Northumberland in an area that had been F&M free for three months. Why has it recurred now after all this time, and why is it spreading so quickly?

DEFRA vets now believe that the source of that outbreak was probably a virus which had lain dormant in a flock of sheep since as long ago as last April. And what has set the alarm bells ringing is that the infection would not have been picked up by the 3 km or 10 km testing regime which is the standard preliminary to lifting restrictions.

It was sheer good fortune that the disease showed up when it did. Had the flock been moved and dispersed – which it could have been in a Foot and Mouth free county – before symptoms reappeared, then the disease could once again have been spread far and wide, with consequences which don't bear thinking about.

The epidemiologists who are driving DEFRA's policy have worked out that if the dispersal as it is called, continues at its present rate, then outbreaks will not stop until Christmas. And if the ratio increases then the epidemic will continue until July next year.

Against this background it is entirely understandable that DEFRA should be seeking to make absolutely certain that only disease free sheep are moved. A number of livestock dispersal sales in clean areas have now had to be cancelled. Several of these were on farm sales of breeding rams.

It appears inevitable that a comprehensive blood-testing programme will be implemented in certain 'suspect' areas of the country.

The Tic beans that we planted in the second week of May have been giving us some cause for concern. We planted the crop too thick on some good land following potatoes lifted this Spring. This, combined with a very good growing season, has meant that we have a crop between five and six feet tall with all the pods and a large part of the stem still green and at least a month to five weeks from combining.

Anyway, we ended up mowing the crop and round baling and wrapping it using extra layers of wrap to avoid puncturing. These bales are being fed to the cows, along with round bale grass silage, and within two days the milk yield rose by 5 per cent. The cows do not like eating the stem, but root around to find all the beans and green pods.

These beans were on part of a field that had a crop of wheat and is due to be planted with Winter barley shortly so at least it tidies the field up by being able to plant it all in one go.

We farmers have, it seems, fallen victim to our own success; sadly, when we should reap benefits from our achievements we end up suffering because we are too good at what we do. In the last 50 years production has doubled but incomes have continued to spiral downwards to an all-time low.

As our productivity climbs ever higher, the profitability plunges – it's all about supply and demand, and the cycle of market economies means the more a farmer produces the greater the supply, the lower the price the less we earn and by earning less we can only maintain our income by growing more.

This chicken and egg cycle is going to be a very hard cycle to break, it's time we all gave some very serious thought to where our industry is going to be in five years' time and how many of us will still be a part of it.

The combining is all finished with rather mixed results – Spring barley and Winter wheat yields were reasonable with the triticale being the season's worst performer. The only hiccup with the combine was a new clutch which was fitted on a wet day so did not cause any delays. There are two possible reasons why the clutch wore – some of our fields are quite steep, and the main one is that the main operator is the Gaffer who is an awful driver.

The first of the turkeys have arrived and, so far, are behaving themselves without any serious pile-ups (deaths from overcrowding and suffocation), but there's plenty of time yet. We have the birds in at four weeks of age and they go straight on to our home-mixed ration. This is blown into bulk hoppers that each hold a ton of feed and the birds eat out of a tray around the bottom. Once a week these hoppers are then taken out of the building by a telescopic loader and replenished. When the birds are young we can get the odd one stuck under the hoppers – unless straw is wedged in, but some still manage it. My job is to sniff them out and let the Missus know who then pulls it out.

We have a few hundred bronze birds for a few supposedly affluent customers, but really it's all a bit of a con as there is absolutely no difference in taste as long as they are fed on the same food.

Farmers are being told to turbocharge their cows with special feeds to help to prevent an impending milk crisis. We could soon be facing a shortage of up to 12 million pints a day because 200,000 dairy cows have been killed during the Foot and Mouth epidemic. We are being told to increase output to avoid large scale imports of milk and milk products.

The latest theory about the origins of the Foot and Mouth outbreak is that it may have come in with a cloud of dust blown in from the Sahara, say scientists. They have linked the outbreak, which started on 20th February, to a massive plume of sand that swirled out of northern Africa several days earlier.

Satellite images show a dust cloud moving over the Atlantic and reaching Britain on 13th February. One week later Foot and Mouth broke out in the UK. Given that the disease's incubation period is seven days, this is one heck of a coincidence.

Spent part of today bathing the combine and baler and spraying them with a mix of oil and diesel before putting them away for the Winter. Some of these machines only get used for a few weeks of the year, but in a season of unsettled weather like this one, it is just too risky to rely on a contractor.

Early start today to get milking finished early so that the Gaffer, Gareth and myself can drive up to Nottingham to the British Potato 2001 harvester demonstration.

A very well organised event and well worth the visit. These days quality is so important as is growing for a specific market. We also went along to a few of the seminars held on the day. The Gaffer was talking to one of the British Potato Council (BPC) staff, who had not seen his name on the list – that's because I sometimes use my maiden name, he said.

I really do wish more provision was made for us travelling canines at service stations.

The old saying of 'pay a bit, owe a bit and keep a bit' is getting much harder to comply with. We seem to be paying a bit, owing a bit but keeping a bit for ourselves is proving nearly impossible.

Sunday 9th September and we have a Vintage working day on one of our fields. The Gaffer gets out one of his tractors and a plough but makes his usual mess – this time the tyres are too wide on the tractor – last year they were at the wrong wheel widths.

There were several tractors that were over 50 years old and in superb condition. One had a six-cylinder engine that was originally in a boat. Another had a single cylinder that you heated before starting with what looked to be a cigarette end.

It is very fortunate that we have these enthusiasts to preserve the old machines to such a high standard so that they are still around in perhaps another 50 years' time for our future generations to enjoy.

We have now sprayed off most of the potato fields to kill the tops. They then need leaving for two to three weeks to allow the skins to set before being lifted and put into store. Virtually all of the Premiere that were planted on the headlands have now been lifted and sold to chip shops, so even if the weather turns wet, it is much easier with the headlands already lifted.

The Government has been accused by its own advisors of mishandling the issue of genetically modified crops. Experts say public concerns over GM foods have been magnified by confusing signals about the role of the latest field trials taking place in the countryside.

Ministers must make it clear that the tests are not the final pieces of the jigsaw needed to allow commercial production to go ahead. The trials on maize, beet and oilseed rape have resulted in unprecedented levels of public demonstration. Crops have been trampled, protestors prosecuted – and cleared – and organic farmers have angrily warned that separation distances between GM and non-GM crops have not been big enough to safeguard their own fields from contamination.

Field trials started in 1999 with a pilot project jointly launched by the Government and the biotechnology industry. It moved to a full scale programme in the Spring of 2000 and is due to end at harvest 2002.

Between 250 and 300 plots ranging from 4 to 30 hectares will eventually be planted for the trial, each area half sown with GM crops, half sown with conventional to allow scientists to evaluate the impact on wildlife of spraying herbicide resistant plants. However, it has been decided there must be more effective consultation on any future trial sites.

The Japanese Government has said it has found the country's – and Asia's – first case of an animal infected with mad cow disease (BSE). Health experts in the country had previously boasted that high standards of cleanliness at Japanese cattle ranches would prevent the country from exposure to the brain eating disease that has afflicted Europe.

Tens of thousands of dairy calves are being shot and buried on farms because the market for them has collapsed due to Foot and Mouth and BSE restrictions. It is estimated that around 200,000 Holstein/Friesian bull calves would be destroyed at birth this year because they have no value, and it would cost money to have them taken away.

Until a few years ago, these dairy bull calves would have been sold to France for veal for £120 - £140 each. People are shooting calves now because by the time they are tagged (costing £3 each) it is cheaper to kill them at birth than sell them for only £1 or £2, that is assuming you can even find a buyer.

We have now burned off all the fields of potatoes with a desiccant. The last two we did still had three or four weeks growth left in them, but we still have

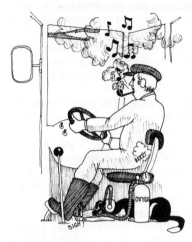

vivid memories of last year's very wet Autumn and Winter with over 10 per cent of the potato acreage not lifted at all. We feel it better to sacrifice some yield in the hope of getting them all lifted.

The Gaffer says that if you are farming the same way now that your father did 25 years ago, either you are wrong now or he was wrong then.

Just out of interest, the slaughter policy for Foot and Mouth has been in operation in the UK since 1834. So one must suspect that after nearly two centuries, perhaps it is not the best route to take.

Gareth has spent a few days ploughing in readiness for corn planting, but he goes too damn fast so I tend to go on the tractor with the Gaffer who is power harrowing which is a much smoother ride. I really do wish he would stop eating so many pickled onions and make the tractor's cab a more pleasant environment.

All the turkeys have now arrived so the Missus and myself are constantly on the go making certain they do not crowd and smother each other. The weather has also turned very cold and showery, so any draughts have to be done away with.

Every so often turkeys go 'walkabout' for no apparent reason, when literally hundreds of them start walking around the shed, always in an anti-clockwise direction. We place wooden pallets in each corner of the building to avoid the ones stuck in the corner being trampled on and suffocated.

All of a sudden the weather has become noticeably colder at night and the grass has almost stopped growing so now all of the young cattle need supplementary feeding of home milled cereals. Like most stock farms we have many 18-24 month old cattle on the farm that we would like to see gone in the next month or so. We probably have enough hay and silage to feed them, but with the buildings full of turkeys, potatoes and cereals, we have no spare accommodation. With our land being on the heavy side, outwintering is not really a viable option.

Foot and Mouth disease has served as a grim wake-up call to the livestock industry to put its house in order. The ease with which this disease, and others in recent years, has taken hold has exposed gaping holes in our on-farm and national biosecurity measures. Even now the straw mats are in shreds and the foot dips are a muddy soup on many farms at a time when we still need to be on our guard.

Our island's defences and market checks fall to many different bodies. These range from the Food Standards Agency and Customs and Excise, to the local authorities and the Meat Hygiene Service.

In spite of the F&M outbreak, little has been done to raise awareness of what can and cannot be legally brought into the UK. Legally travellers can bring in up to 1 kg of cooked meat in hermetically sealed containers for their own consumption, yet people are bringing in all kinds of meat products, including the increasingly popular 'bush meat' from Africa, where Foot and Mouth and other diseases including the deadly ebola virus are endemic.

However, the current shortcomings of illegal import controls are no excuse to let biosecurity slip at farm level. We may need to consider double fencing on farm boundaries to prevent direct contact between animals on neighbouring farms, just as we did over 50 years ago to control the spread of TB. We may have to look at the facilities and access for delivery vehicles and milk tankers. There is no point expecting lorries to be clean when they arrive, if they are expected to drive over, or park on, dirty concrete.

The only way farming can survive after F&M and BSE is for more trust between the producer and the consumer. We are therefore going to have to see more farm assurance schemes, more stringent health checks and more paperwork. The older, more complacent, farmers will absolutely hate this new approach and will be only too pleased to leave the industry to the younger generation who have been brought up with control measures anyway.

All of our yearling rams have now been sold privately and have left the farm, so now the only ones to moan at me are the two senior stock rams, Jim and Adam, and this year's crop of ram lambs. We try not to sell any ram lambs if possible, preferring to take them all on to yearlings. However, if anyone is desperately in need a few may go.

This last week has seen the catastrophic collapse of the twin towers of the World Trade Centre in New York after planes were deliberately flown into them and also the Pentagon Building in Washington. There has been a dreadful loss of life and the whole world is absolutely stunned by these unnecessary acts of violence.

Several fields of wheat and barley have just been planted, rolled and pre-emergence sprayed, before we get really stuck in to potato lifting. Gareth has banned the Gaffer off the corn drill as he cannot even drive straight anymore, so we end up on the power harrow or rolling instead, which anyway is much easier.

There is a great divide between farmers who had stock and those whose farms were empty. Those with no stock had to face the problem of whether to buy new stock, or deal with having no work to do, while those whose animals had escaped slaughter had other problems. They have a lot of extra stock that they can't sell, a shortage of Winter feed and a negative cash flow. At the moment the banks are being very supportive, but when they see a business is not viable what is the point in allowing it to continue.

The whole of Scotland is now officially classed as disease free from Foot and Mouth. Wales has had no outbreaks confirmed for over 30 days which is the longest disease free period since the outbreak first began over six months ago. There have been no new cases of the disease in the UK for the last three days which is encouraging news, but still gives us no scope to relax.

The Missus tells me I need to broaden my horizons as the only experience I have is farming and shopkeeping. Backpacking around the world is not really an option for a canine like myself and a change is out of the question as I enjoy my present existence, but any opportunity to gain experience and make extra money needs serious consideration with the present financial state of agriculture.

Tracey's boyfriend Moose is a builder, so it has been decided that I spend a few days with him and his mate Craig on a building site to broaden my horizons.

An early start in his van so that we are at the site by the time it comes light. What they are building are factory units on a new industrial site alongside a wood and a disused refuse tip and the first smell to greet me is the divine fragrance of a very large rodent population. Moose and I are big mates and as I get out of his van, he says to me, 'We leave at 6 pm this evening, Benny, so have a good day's ratting'.

Moose and Craig get the concrete mixer going and start laying blocks within minutes of arriving. It seems they are on piecework – you get paid by the number of blocks or bricks that you lay so the faster you work, the more money you earn.

Several more gangs have arrived by now – some bricking, some steel erectors, carpenters, plumbers, etc. The total workforce must be nearly 50 and by 9 o'clock a hot dog van arrives at the site and we all stop for a quick bacon sarnie and a cup of tea, or can of coke in my case.

Just as we start up work again this big guy turns up wearing a hard hat and carrying plans of the site, and a real miserable looking so-and-so he is. Apparently, he is the site foreman who makes life hell for all the workers on the site. He comes straight up to Moose and Craig demanding, 'Who does this flaming mutt belong to? And has he been vaccinated?' I'm thinking to myself, unless you get rid of that attitude problem of yours buddy boy, I'll be vaccinating you with my teeth.

Rather than cause a scene, I decide to explore the site and have a day's ratting. Meet up with another canine on the site belonging to a gang of builders. His name is L.B. which is short for Little Bugger and he is a terrier whose main aim in life is ratting.

At the back of the site are a number of portable toilets with one of them being the absolute in luxury with what seems like noise insulation and I can only assume it is for the sole use of the site manager.

L.B. and myself then make for this disused refuse tip and there are rats everywhere. We spent the first couple of hours reducing their numbers in no uncertain terms, then this one enormous rat made a break for freedom to the building site with my mate and I in hot pursuit. Up a wooden plank he ran and did a disappearing act into the centre of a cavity wall with bricks the one side and blocks on the other with wire ties in between.

'I can get him by balancing on the wire ties', says L.B. Before I have a chance to ask him how he thought he was going to get out, L.B. had disappeared into the darkness. By this time 'clever dick', the foreman, had arrived and went absolutely ape with me for leading L.B. astray.

Within minutes L.B. told me that he was well and truly trapped between these two walls and he could not even turn around, and he had completely lost track of the rat.

'Only one thing for it,' says L.B.'s owner, 'we'll have to cut a hole in the bottom of the wall and coax him out.'

'We can't do that', says the boss man, 'we'll slide in a long narrow piece of timber at an angle and persuade him to walk up it.' After over an hour nothing had happened at all.

One of the guys working on the site had a brother in the fire service and they had just taken delivery of a new heat seeking device that he knew they would just love to try out. In a very short time, the firemen arrived quickly followed by a TV crew, the RSPCA and the police. By this time, the boss man was really throwing his toys out of the pram so I kept well out of his way.

Within minutes the fire crew had located L.B., his owner cut a hole in the inner wall, and our little hero walked to safety to rounds of applause. As this was going out live on TV, out of the hole ran that pesky rat so once more we are in hot pursuit back to the refuse tip but we soon lose him down one of the many holes.

By this time it is late afternoon and I have taken up my post behind a pallet of bricks stacked next to the super duper mobile toilet. Shortly the boss man arrived and closes the door. I get on top of the stack of bricks and slip a wall tie into the door handle to stop the miserable sod coming out. I leave him in there for a couple of hours, then pull the tie out with my teeth and disappear with the boss man not knowing who had played a trick on him.

My first day as a builder's mate had been really exciting but in future I think I will stick to my day job.

On the way home, Moose and I stopped for a drink – him a pint of beer and me a can of coke. He was highly amused by my escapades today as were his workmates, but we decided my next day out on the building site was when the site manager was on holiday.

When we got home the Gaffer and the Missus were thrilled to have seen me on the television, chasing the rat that had caused all the trouble in the first place.

Back at Faulty Farm the language sometimes leaves something to be desired, but there is one four letter word that fills me with absolute fear – BATH. Most weeks Tracey decides I need a bath, so a bath it has to be. Why ever has nobody developed a soap or shampoo that does not sting your eyes.

Also it wouldn't be so bad if it was last thing at night before I go to bed – but no, it can be any time of day. Even though she dries me afterwards, it is a weekly experience I would be happy to forego. My natural instinct after being dried is to find a distinctive aroma to roll in to stop me smelling so unmasculine.

Wednesday 19th September and it's the Dairy Event at Stoneleigh – one of my favourite days out. Gaffer milks early and as he comes in for breakfast he delivers some devastating news. 'Sorry Benny, you can't come along today due to the Foot and Mouth regulations.'

I just could not believe what I was hearing but could tell by the old feller's voice that he meant it. The Missus had the hoover cleaning out the car and I could see this was my chance. First, however, I find a white stick, a pair of shades and my lead and hide them in the back of the car and then I climb under a coat in the back and stowaway out of sight.

A quick breakfast and the Gaffer and Gareth climb in ready for an early getaway. 'Where's Benny', the Gaffer asks the Missus. 'Ratting as usual, I suppose,' says she.

It's away we go – the A40, M50, M5 and it's quite interesting listening in to their conversations. I wait until we've covered at least 50 miles in case they turn around and take me home, before I creep out from under the coat and lick the old boy on the back of his neck. Rather than being annoyed, they both think it highly amusing.

We get to Stoneleigh and enter the site via very strict biosecurity measures.

Missus phones up Gareth on his mobile to say she can't find me – 'I'm not surprised', says he, 'he'd stowed away in the car and is with us'. I pass the Gaffer his white stick and shades and my lead so I can pretend to be his guide dog.

No cattle at the event this year for obvious reasons. The Gaffer seems to meet somebody he knows every 50 yards so progress is rather slow. One rep comments that he didn't realise he needed a guide dog. 'You obviously haven't seen him driving', says Gareth. They stop to pig out on cups of tea, cakes, burgers and cans of coke at ever so many trade stands.

One very interesting feature this year is the different makes of Robotic Milkers, which must be the way forward with the extreme shortage of skilled herdspersons in the country.

The Council for the Protection of Rural England (CPRE) has said Ministers had failed to understand the modern economy of the countryside. The Government response to Foot and Mouth was more damaging than the disease itself. The initial response to 'close the countryside' was based on the misnomer of a separate 'rural economy' isolated from the rest of the economy. It failed to appreciate how much businesses other than agriculture also rely on a high quality countryside. As a result, many businesses, in town and country, have experienced tremendous hardship and economic difficulties. The CPRE report found the disease, and the Government's policies, adversely affected 40 per cent of rural businesses.

We keep hearing of agricultural land being used for energy crops, i.e. oilseed rape used for production of bio-diesel and mycanthus (elephant grass) and other quick growing crops used in power stations to generate electricity. Did you know that 100 years ago 20 per cent of agricultural crops were used for fuel and transport? – hay and oats to feed the horses!

DEFRA has stated that livestock markets and farm sales of livestock will probably not reopen this year, putting an end to competitive selling.

The average price of beef per kilo deadweight at the moment is 154 pence for top quality. The Irish have been unloading large volumes of beef diverted from the Continent because of the BSE issue and it would appear that certain supermarket chains have been only too happy to buy it, making a complete mockery of their supposed loyalty to the British producer. Even those supermarkets which have stuck by their British suppliers have still been only too happy to use the availability of cheap Irish beef to force the prices down. Whether the situation would be any better if the auction marts were still operating is debatable.

The fact that the retailers and abattoirs between them appear to be exploiting the poor old producer at a time when there is no alternative to deadweight sales, is doing nothing for the arguments of those people who call for stronger, more transparent partnerships in the food chain.

The big boys will keep squeezing until the British supply is reduced to the extent that the supermarkets can claim that they simply have to switch to cheaper imports.

We've been flat out potato bulking for the last week or so. The ground is very dry and in these conditions the skins take longer to set. Any fields on a bank, as most of ours are, we are just lifting uphill at the moment to avoid damage to the spuds if they spend too much time going up the main web.

As we fill the store a high volume PTO fan on the back of one of the Gaffer's vintage tractors is going almost non-stop blowing air at the clamp face or boxes to get the spuds completely dry to help long term storage.

Foot and Mouth scare back to haunt us today. An immediate neighbour of some off-lying land where we have our ewes sent some lambs off to Ross-on-Wye market, which is being used as a collection centre, and ulcers were found in their mouths. These lambs plus 140 others were slaughtered as a precaution. At the moment we are all anxiously awaiting the results of blood tests.

Up to 40 million sheep in the UK could be slaughtered over a 5-year period if BSE was discovered in the UK flock. So far no BSE cases in sheep have been discovered. A surveillance programme is under way aimed at looking for BSE in the national flock, made up of 20 million adult sheep and 20 million lambs.

Shoppers could see the price of their daily pinta rise by a penny as farmers launch a new bid to drive up the price of milk, which is still the cheapest in Europe. Analysts are warning that the Foot and Mouth crisis could lead to a major milk shortage this winter.

The supermarkets say they are prepared to increase prices if the money goes back to the producers but the processors say a price increase to farmers is not justified.

Farmers are currently getting a maximum of 18 pence a litre for their milk while leading analysts say the true cost of production is nearer 20 pence per litre. Most weeks in the farming press we see some smug producer, backed up by an independent consultant, claiming they can produce milk for 18 pence a litre or less. Just who do they think they are kidding?

We have just been informed that the suspected case of Foot and Mouth on one of our neighbour's holdings is negative, which is a huge relief.

The 1st October and farmers will today launch a major campaign to combat a steady tide of illegal meat imports threatening to unleash more animal health problems in the UK. They will be picketing at channel ports and a 30,000 signature petition will be handed in at the Labour Party Conference in Brighton.

Farmers are becoming fed up with being lectured to on biosecurity while the Government does nothing to police illegal imports of meat. We have to minimise the risk of the disease being imported and we are as much at risk now as we were when the virus arrived here in February.

Despite the farmers' campaign, supermarkets in the UK are still selling beef from Zimbabwe and Botswana – both countries where the disease is epidemic.

Exporters have been known to exploit EU law, which allows free movement within the community once imports have crossed its border. That allows them to send shipments in through the point of least resistance where port controls are at their most lax, and then ship them into the UK.

DEFRA Farm Minister Margaret Beckett has said the existing CAP had been an abject failure. 'You could say that no one is happy', she said. Farmers' incomes were running at half the national average, consumer confidence had been hit by repeated food scares, and environmentalists were even more dissatisfied.

The Government wants an end to milk quotas and set-aside and a partial re-nationalisation of European farm policy, as it attempts to reshape the CAP. Until we break out of the stranglehold of milk quotas, the industry is never going to achieve its true potential they claim. Once quotas are done away with we all produce more milk and the price will drop, which is good news for the electorate.

They also want an end to set-aside, which would lead to a surplus of grain, and falling grain prices – again good for the electorate.

We are being told to change our ways, or die. From now on we are to be stewards of the countryside, with production subsidies phased out and replaced by environmental subsidies.

Foot and Mouth has put paid to some of the most popular events in the farming calendar – the Christmas Fatstock Shows. These are held in early December and offer farmers a Winter showcase for their animals. The events are staged to sell animals for the Christmas trade with butchers decorating their windows with the rosettes from the winners they have bought.

You would not normally think of arable farmers as the poor relations of British farming (the old barley baron image as enthusiastically promoted by Oliver Walston dies hard), but their incomes have actually fallen further and faster over the last six years than any other sector, barring lowland beef and sheep.

The reasons are painfully obvious; a strong currency, compounded by a lousy harvest. Corn prices are actually slightly stronger than last year, but not to anything like the extent which would make up for the lowest wheat acreage and the worst yields for many years.

Has Margaret Beckett read 'Alice in Wonderland'? Anyone listening to her speech at the Labour Party Conference in Brighton could be forgiven for thinking that her words owed much to the topsy-turvy logic of Lewis Carroll's fable. For evidence look no further than her tenuous grasp of the harsh realities of farming life and food production. Consumers are no longer prepared to pay high prices for food, she told the conference. What high prices?

In the real world, as a percentage of national income Britons pay less than ever before for top-quality, welfare-friendly British food. The weekly food shopping bill accounts for only 9 per cent of disposable income compared with 20 per cent 40 years ago.

Not only must our 'high' food prices fall, but farmers must become market orientated and customer focused as farm support changes. How does she think UK farmers can continue to produce top quality food at bargain basement prices? How can we deliver not only the highest welfare standards in the world, while maintaining our rich and varied countryside, without reasonable prices, fair competition or financial support from Whitehall or Brussels?

What is even more curious is that no one challenged her views. No one questioned the wisdom of making CAP reform her top priority at a time when morale and incomes in rural Britain are so low. No one highlighted that without farm support, food prices would rise unless we are prepared to scour the dustbins of the world for imports.

No one denies the need for change and for farmers to improve their links with consumers, but Mrs Beckett's Alice in Wonderland vision of British farming's future would bring no happy ending. Rather it would open a nightmare chapter in our farming history.

The NFU is under pressure to improve its Little Red Tractor campaign after a poll found that country of origin is a low priority for consumers when buying food. Only 3 per cent of consumers believe country of origin is an important factor that influences the food they buy, revealed a poll by the Food Standards Agency. Instead, respondents clearly rate price ahead of taste, quality, health issues and production methods. Country of origin came almost bottom of the list.

Today is 7th October and the country has just been seven days without a single case of Foot and Mouth disease, so we are all keeping our fingers and everything else crossed that it may at last be coming to an end. However, out of 3,500 sheep tested on Exmoor recently, four were found to have Foot and Mouth anti-bodies. As these sheep were not tagged nobody knows who the four belong to so it is a very worrying time in that area once more.

Accusations of a cover-up of F&M were levelled at the Government this week after it emerged British vets warned colleagues overseas about the disease three months before the outbreak was publicly announced. Canadian officials say they imposed border checks last December after being tipped off that there was a danger of the disease crossing the Atlantic, weeks before the first case was confirmed on 20th February.

With opposition spokesmen renewing calls for a full, independent inquiry, it has been revealed that the Minister sacked by Tony Blair over the crisis blames Downing Street for the disaster. Nick Brown, who was made the fall guy for the debacle and demoted from the Cabinet, wants to go on the record and clear his name and those of the officials at the disbanded MAFF – potentially causing grave embarrassment to Tony Blair.

Mr Brown is keen to publish his future evidence to the three Foot and Mouth inquiries being held behind closed doors, to help prove that the department was coping admirably until Downing Street took over a month into the crisis. He has said that he thinks it is better to put his evidence in private, but he could then publish a transcript afterwards. The enquiry will have to consider the damning new evidence that the Foot and Mouth problem began long before the Government has admitted.

Rugby teams from our country that had played in rural areas in Britain had to have themselves and their kit disinfected when they arrived in Canada. When asked why they were told by an airport official – 'Because you have Foot and Mouth in England.' When they were told it was not true the Canadian official said, 'If your Government chooses not to tell you, that's up to them, but you have'.

The fact is we will never know who knew what, and when they knew it, until there is a full independent public inquiry.

We would have been able to detect the disease much earlier if the Government had not allowed the network of vets and inspectors to wither away. The relationship between ministry and private vets had also broken down.

The first 2½ weeks of potato lifting went by with only one day missed due to the weather, but now we have ground to a halt for the last three days with over 50 mm of rain in 48 hours. So now it's back to grading spuds and routine stock and turkey duties. The turkeys seem to be growing at a good rate and now are up to eating five tons a week with grit mixed in the feed, and also in self-feed hoppers.

Even though we are still classed as a 'high risk' county, we can now move our own stock around to different blocks of land that we farm ourselves, subject to a biosecurity check by our own vet to see if our and our neighbour's stock cannot touch, either through or over a fence or hedge. We have spent some time recently erecting double fences to make certain we qualify. This will mean that heifers can be brought back home to the bull, breeding ewes and ram lambs can be moved to forage rape for grazing and store cattle can be kept in smaller numbers, to avoid poaching, as the weather deteriorates.

The total number of Foot and Mouth cases now stands at 2,030, but with no new cases for 10 days.

Very warm sunny day today with bright sunlight after three days of no sunshine at all, so the turkeys are all very agitated and decide to go 'walkabout'. Almost every bird in each of the four sheds walking anti-clockwise around the sheds and making an awful din, with some cannibalism occurring as well.

Extra straw spread on the ground makes no difference so Gareth and I shoot up to the farmers co-operative in the village for some bales of wood shavings and within no time at all they have all settled down and peace returns to Faulty Farm.

Vets have slaughtered 1,700 sheep amid mounting evidence that Foot and Mouth had penetrated an area that had been thought to be free of the disease. Random tests on the flock, based inside the Exmoor National Park, showed one sheep carrying virus anti-bodies, and a further 25 animals were 'inconclusive'. They are now checking blood samples to see if any of the slaughtered animals had the active virus.

When the Food Standards Agency (FSA) decided to check out DEFRA regarding the problem of whether BSE has got into sheep, it found that the sheep brains various laboratories have been testing revealed evidence of the BSE prion protein dating from 1990, but none in samples collected in 1995 or more recently. Which suggests that, while BSE in sheep might once have been a problem, it no longer is, making it more difficult for DEFRA to justify a mass cull.

We are now on our fifth day of being rained off land work and the Gaffer is going around with a face like a bulldog chewing a wasp. However, the weather is slowly improving so we will soon be back outside rather than spending most of our time potato grading.

Back on field work at last. Gareth is ploughing and planting corn and the Gaffer and myself are power harrowing. As the Autumn is setting in, the leaves on the trees are changing colour on an almost daily basis. Every day I see squirrels collecting nuts ready for their Winter hibernation and, even though I regularly give chase, I have yet to catch one of the pesky things.

None of the young stock have yet been housed for the Winter, but are all being fed cereals and silage or hay as the grass growth slows down.

By now virtually all the ewes are in lamb to either Jim or Adam, and are looking in excellent condition. The dairy cows are still out night and day, but are now on virtually full Winter rations.

The turkeys are growing fairly well, with the exception of one batch that need to kill out (oven ready weight) at 13-14 lb. by Christmas, so we have bought in a load of pellets to speed up their growth rate to achieve their target weight.

Last night I was up the shop in the village helping Tracey with the late shift, seated on my usual perch behind the counter. In walked this stunning, recently married, farmer's daughter called Jo who said to me, 'Hi, Benny, how's the book coming along?' Well you could have knocked me over with a feather as I thought it was all a big secret. It wasn't as if I was even writing at the time.

We've just had a visit from the VAT man. When he first rang up, the Gaffer said his office hours were before 6.30 in the morning and after 7.30 at night. This managed to put him off for a few months before he made a definite appointment. An hour before he was due, the old boy half filled a bag with silage and hid it behind the chair in the office.

After less than one hour in the office the VAT man emerged looking pale and stinking of silage and said he had seen enough. It was a full two days before the office was habitable.

At last some of the dairy consultancy groups have come to their senses and stopped quoting unit costs of production per litre, as the major dairies use them to drag down the milk price. It's taken these guys a long time to realise what everyone else has been aware of for decades.

There appears to be a general consensus in the dairy industry that there will be no general price rise this Autumn, indeed some of the major dairies that have been top performers for the Summer are having to reduce their prices, albeit marginally.

Britain's farmers are facing debt and despair as they struggle to survive on less than £7 per day. In the past six years the average income from a 500 acre lowland farm has plummeted from £80,000 to £2,500 per annum. That means a take home wage of just 70p per hour for farmers working 10 hours a day, seven days a week. These figures are generous compared to some smaller livestock farms. As a result, a new generation of farmers are refusing to take on family businesses, and who can blame them.

A new report in the *British Medical Journal* by Dr George Venters says a link between new variant CJD and BSE in cows is unlikely. He claims the relatively low number of confirmed cases of the human form of the disease was the 'most telling' evidence and cast doubt on a connection.

He says the explosion in mad cow disease cases in livestock between 1983 and 1988 should have been paralleled by a rise in cases of its human form if one had caused the other.

He claims the new variant CJD might not be new at all and might merely have come from the original CJD, first found in 1913. He says, 'There is no clear evidence and the existing criteria used to establish the links between BSE and new variant CJD are far from robust. The epidemiology shows the link is actually not likely'.

Farmers are preparing to take the Government to court if their call for a public inquiry into Foot and Mouth is refused. A letter calling for a public hearing has been sent on their behalf to DEFRA Secretary of State, Margaret Beckett. If the Government refuses to grant a full inquiry, legal proceedings for a judicial review will begin. Farmers from all over the country who had suffered in the crisis are expected to join in.

Scientists who only weeks ago were fearing they may have evidence of BSE in the brains of sheep, leading to the destruction of the entire UK sheep population, have now admitted the brain samples they were investigating did not belong to sheep at all but to cattle. The blunder is a huge embarrassment for ministers and the government-funded institute in Pirbright, Surrey, which carried out the work on the back of a £217,000 payment from taxpayers.

Research on whether BSE exists in the national sheep flock has been minimal – with only 180 animals tested out of 40 million and yet they were still talking of mass slaughter!

However, we still do not know if lamb is really safe to eat at the end of a five year project, which has now been rendered worthless. More work needs to be carried out to breed sheep that are resistant to scrapie and the sooner the better.

One of the latest EU directives seeks to limit tractor driving to only two or three hours per day, due to vibrations causing injuries to the lower back. It appears that more up to date tractors with front axle and cab suspension would mean more hours could be spent driving. This piece of legislation would appeal to the Gaffer as it is difficult to persuade him to do more than a few hours per day anyway.

One thing that really gets up my nose are squirrels. At the edge of our lawn is a walnut tree and at the moment they are flat out gathering the nuts for their Winter hibernation and I can almost hear the little gits laughing at me, knowing they are quite safe.

Margaret Beckett has pledged a £24 million boost for businesses suffering due to Foot and Mouth. The move follows the publication of rural recovery co-ordinator Lord Haskins' report of the effects of the outbreak in Cumbria.

Cumbria will take the 'lions share' of the money which will be allocated through regional development agencies, but other parts of the country would benefit as well. It will be used to promote recovery of the tourism and small businesses economy. It may just be enough for some hotels and shops to apply a coat of paint, which all helps.

At the beginning of 2001 we dared to allow ourselves to believe that after five years of troubles things were slowly beginning to improve. Then on 20th February disaster struck again. But in the midst of this gloom and despair we must keep our eyes on the future. Fighting our way out of Foot and Mouth will be tough enough. Fighting for a better future once the spectre of this disease is finally behind us will be even tougher.

Tony Blair's attempt to hush up details of the Foot and Mouth shambles is set to be torpedoed this week when the European Parliament votes to hold a public inquiry into the affair. Tory MEPs are spearheading a plan to summon ministers and officials to Brussels to defend their decisions under the glare of public scrutiny. They have the backing of other concerned Europeans who fear further outbreaks in the UK and are astonished that Labour is continuing to resist calls for the full details of the disaster to be made public.

This investigation by the European Parliament will be fully public and can call witnesses and demand access to documents – exactly what the British Government wants to avoid.

EU member states are very concerned about the lack of frontier controls on Foot and Mouth by the UK, and the lack of control at ports and airports in the EU. MEPs in other EU countries are simply astonished that Britain has allowed this to drag on so long without a full public inquiry. Their own livestock industries remain potentially under threat until the truth is established.

British consumers have been accused of operating dual-standards – supporting the call for better welfare on farms but refusing to pay for it. This means that shoppers are inadvertently condoning poor welfare. All shoppers claim they want to buy welfare friendly products – but when it comes to the supermarket checkouts, they are simply not putting their money where their mouths are. This leaves many high welfare farmers high and dry, having invested heavily in good welfare practice, with no marketplace for their products.

It is fast getting to the stage that British farmers will soon find it impossible to compete on world markets, as a result of welfare pressures.

Two reports have just been published this week on how to help farming and the rural economy recover from the Foot and Mouth crisis.

The one is full of waffle, with large sections devoted to what the Government has done in the past, and very little on what needs to be done in the future. This report was compiled by a group of farming and tourism leaders operating as the Rural Task Force.

The other report is concise, hard-headed and demonstrates a shrewd awareness of the nature and causes of the crisis in the countryside and makes a series of sensible suggestions. This report is written by none other than Lord Haskins, who has allowed himself to be portrayed as Farming Enemy Number One.

He remains as firmly opposed as ever to the application of further subsidies as a cure for farming ills. He does, however, understand that without help to get them through the short-term, many small farms and businesses will not be around for very much longer. Hence the first priority is getting people through this coming Winter.

He says we need forbearance from the Banks, the Inland Revenue and Customs and Excise and maintaining this for a number of years. Also, he wants free farm consultancy for ex-Form D farms, and special compensation for farmers who cannot sell store stock because of continuing movement restrictions.

The Foot and Mouth epidemic has to date cost DEFRA £1.567 billion, excluding the cost of the Livestock Welfare Disposal Scheme. £1.051 billion has been paid out to farmers as compensation, which also includes £348 million paid to contractors.

As of 31st July, the Defence Ministry had charged the Department £5.34 million for overtime, allowances, travel and subsistence costs. The full cost of the epidemic to the Defence Ministry was expected to be approximately an additional £12 million, but the full cost would not be known for some time.

Our county has now been classified as 'at risk', rather than 'high risk' as regards Foot and Mouth regulations, which means we can now move stock out of the county (under licence) to other at risk counties, so the situation is very slowly improving. Many more counties in the UK are now classified as 'Foot and Mouth free'. However, 'multiple pick-ups' of stock are still not allowed which makes it very difficult and expensive for smaller farms without the numbers of stock to fill a load.

At the beginning of September we cut, baled and wrapped a field of late sown Spring beans for whole-crop silage. The young stock and cows manage to pick out and eat virtually all the pods and beans, but will not eat the haulm, which is not really surprising. However, the heap of unused bales is causing a problem for the Gaffer and Gareth but is creating a recreational adventure for myself. The reason – RATS, they absolutely love the stuff and are playing havoc with the bales. Every spare moment I get I am now rat catching. The young ones are fairly easy prey but not so with the older ones.

This last week has been almost constant heavy rain with no land work done at all – we are mostly potato grading. Only a mediocre sale of Ware potatoes but an excellent trade for good chipping Maris Piper. At the moment we are supplying 12 fish and chip shops. Most of these guys sell just over a ton a week each of chips so I normally go on two deliveries each night in the van with Gareth after milking.

Just lately I have been wondering what would be an appropriate Christmas present for the Gaffer. Well, he's been erecting some new rails around the car park (not to a very high standard) and I've decided to buy him a new bubble for his spirit level.

The review of tractor driving hours which only last week was being strongly debated, has now been postponed for five years so we may still be able to get the occasional day's work out of the old feller for a few more years yet.

Hundreds of mink have just escaped from a farm in the New Forest area of Hampshire after suspected animal rights activists opened the doors of their cages. In 1998 nearly 6,000 were set free from the same farm in what can only be described as utterly irresponsible action due to the complete devastation of natural wildlife.

Keeping mink and other animals for slaughter for their fur was banned under the Fur Farming (Prohibition) Act 2000. Fur farmers, however, have until 1st January, 2003 to wind down their businesses.

Tracey keeps telling me that I need to broaden my horizons so it has been decided that I have a day with that smoothy Jake (Sandra and Carl's Labrador) as a trainee gun dog. I'm not really very fond of guns anyway but it seems all has been decided and a day with Carl and Jake it has to be. The first part of the day will be spend just finding game and vermin and perhaps later in the afternoon Carl will use his gun and teach me the art of retrieving.

I didn't realise that guns can only be effective at up to about 40 yards, so we cannot go too far ahead of Carl but must work close to him. After a few hours Jake had put several pheasants, ducks and pigeons to flight and he thought this was just brilliant. I had found three scents of rats, but had not been allowed to dig them out which all seems such a waste.

By now I am becoming completely bored with this whole concept of pretending to be a big game hunting gun dog and have decided on my own game plan.

By now Carl is carrying his gun so I decide to go further ahead than necessary to flush out the birds and rabbits so they will be out of shot gun range, which managed to lose me many brownie points.

Eventually Carl has a shot at a pigeon and I decide to do a runner and pretend to be afraid. The more he calls me the faster I run in the opposite direction. This managed to conclude my one and only adventures as a wannabe gun dog which was a huge relief. My ultimate hunting adventure is a good ratting session either on my own or with another like-minded canine.

An independent inquiry into the handling of the foot and mouth crisis in Devon has stated the Government's handling of the crisis was lamentable. Witnesses told how culls were bungled, farmers treated appallingly and the needs of the local communities ignored.

The report claims that 'carnage by computer' had entire herds slaughtered where there was no risk of infection. It calls for the Army to be put in charge of any future outbreak. Experts say funeral pyres used to dispose of the carcasses damaged the tourism industry beyond belief and must never be used again.

The inquiry, set up by Devon County Council, heard from 50 witnesses and received 360 submissions from people from all walks of life including farmers, clergy and businessmen.

We've got several cows and heifers calving at the moment to that dopey Limousin bull of ours, Malcolm. One cow that had a fairly difficult calving, complicated by milk fever, did not get up for two days. Anyway, her calf, which was fine, followed me around for two days just because I was the one who had licked it first and it thought I was its mother.

When its mother did recover, she was having none of that and I was soon chased out of the shed by her in no uncertain terms – talk about a big, furry, hairy creature.

Just lately we've had some quite serious potato grading sessions with another one, or perhaps two, of Gareth's mates drafted in for the day. The Gaffer spends most of the day carting in loads from our off-lying farm five miles away, where the spuds are stored.

When the old boy gets back here he can't resist having a go on the bags, until the others say to him, 'You are the weakest link, Goodbye', so off he obediently goes to get another load, quite often taking me with him.

In the last three weeks the price of fuel has dropped by between 10 per cent and 15 per cent, which is very welcome. At the pumps now, white diesel is 73 or 74 pence a litre and petrol just on or slightly above 70 pence per litre.

November

Already we are into the penultimate month of the year after the mildest October since records began. It has also been one of the wettest Octobers on record. Due to the mild weather and no frost, all the leaves are still on the trees and the grass is still growing. One of our neighbours with a large acreage of cider apples says the picking off the floor by harvester has been much easier than normal due to the absence of leaves.

We have now been over 30 days without a single case of Foot and Mouth in the UK and are gradually seeing a relaxation of livestock movement restrictions. We have now been granted a 'Sole Occupancy Licence' to move stock around different blocks of land. However, once you have moved stock you cannot move any more for 21 days but you can move several batches on the one day.

£57 million of Agrimonetary Compensation due to arable farmers because of the strength of the pound against the Euro has not been claimed from the EU by our own Government, as the Government would have had to come up with the same figure itself. This money would have been worth £12.50 per hectare for all combinable crops and is much needed in the present economic climate.

Now that our county is classified as Low Risk – the same as many neighbouring counties - we have managed to sell another lorry load of 22-month-old continental heifers so easing the pressure on winter housing. From the day of purchase to collection was only three days. The vet has to inspect them 24 hours before collection, a licence is issued by our local Trading Standards Officer and the purchaser must make an appointment to have his lorry cleaned and disinfected and sealed at an approved premises. So a large number of phone calls, faxes and mountains of paperwork, but every department working very hard to get livestock movements under way before there is a serious animal welfare problem.

The breeding ewes and Jim and Adam now have access to a field of forage rape planted a few months ago to supplement their grazing. They still have 'run-back' onto a field of grass. The old dears are looking quite heavy in lamb already, with two months to go before the start of lambing.

This year's ram lambs have also been drenched and moved onto forage rape. There are a couple of them who really try my patience by standing up to me so they have to be shown who's boss, or next year they will show me no respect at all.

The weather is gradually improving so we are back corn planting but conditions are far from perfect so we have increased the seed rate to compensate. We have now finished corn planting for the year, with the earlier-sown fields looking quite well. As the Winter is setting in the crows are starting to get hungry, so the later-sown fields require bird scarers to be erected to help me out.

We still have a few days potato lifting in one very heavy field but as yet it won't go. It was intended to lift this field earlier but the skins had not set due to the Gaffer being too late burning them off. I seem to remember the same thing happening last year and he still hasn't learnt his lesson. I say if you're had once it's bad luck, but if you're had a second time you're a mug.

We have also mowed two fields for silage that were inaccessible to the cows. At this time of the year getting any degree of wilting at all is nearly impossible due to the fog not lifting until mid-morning. An absence of wind and sun often means it is early afternoon before baling can commence. The bales are extremely heavy and overloading of trailers will result in punctures, so we are going with only part loads.

It's the 5th November and Guy Fawkes day. For some weeks now ourselves and many other locals have been taking broken pallets, timber and any other debris that will burn, to build this enormous bonfire on the village green in

readiness for the big occasion. It has become obvious to myself that this mound of timber, etc. has become home to a large rodent population.

We milk early and arrive in the village well before the light-up time, so the Gaffer and I can start to pig out on burgers and coke. The evening is dry but very cold, and as there is a bank on the one side of the village green, this is being used as a drive-in bonfire party and people can stay in their vehicles and watch the fireworks. When the bonfire is lit I am right at the front of the crowd waiting for the first rodents to break cover. They start to bolt – I kill the first, miss two others, catch another one and with that out runs this enormous rat, nearly the size of a cat and boy can he run fast. Through the crowd, through the drive-in vehicles and in through the open door of a mini-bus full of students. Well, I've never known such hysteria – it's only a damn rat, I've never seen people evacuate a vehicle so quickly.

Three times around the mini-bus, twice I just got hold of the end of his tail, then out through the door and across to the allotments. I realise if he gets in there and under one of the garden sheds, he's safe – so into turbo boost and I just catch him before he reached freedom.

This is one of the biggest rats I have ever seen so decide to take him back for the Gaffer to see, not realising the effect it will have on the crowd, after all it is dead, but I notice a rabbit hole and drop it down out of sight. By this time there are fireworks exploding, rockets launching and all sorts of whistling and banging noises and shrieks of delight from the crowd. It never ceases to amaze me how frightened some people are of rats – after all they are not likely to attack them, in fact the rat is probably more frightened than they are.

The lack of young farmers entering the industry is a very real cause for concern. Farming is hardly a great advert for attracting new recruits after a succession of crises.

Agricultural colleges have seen the number of students fall by up to 30 per cent and students can be up to £10,000 in debt by the end of their course. The Government must realise the importance of farming to our economy and everyday life. Without a new generation coming through to take the industry forward, farming in Britain will collapse.

Fears that up to one million lightweight lambs would have to be disposed of under the Livestock Welfare Disposal Scheme have proved unfounded. New figures show that 600,000 such lambs had to be disposed of in this way. The rest, which are usually sold to Mediterranean countries, ended up on British supermarket shelves thanks to a high profile marketing strategy.

In fact, new figures have revealed that UK consumption of lamb in the past two to three months has been higher than for many years, which bodes well for the future.

One in eight British workers takes a dog to work, and it has been proven that being in the company of pets helps to reduce stress levels and lower blood pressure. Many employers are now adopting a dog-friendly policy and it appears if it's a dog-friendly company it's also people-friendly as well.

I've just read in one of my monthly canine magazines that the most popular name for a dog is the one I was given – Ben, closely followed by Max, Bonnie and Sam. In fact one in 30 canines is called Ben.

It is now into the second week of November and the weather is still dry and very mild so we have just spent the last two days finishing potato lifting. We needed two four-wheel drive tractors to pull the harvester the whole time but eventually the job is completed for another year. The spuds are quite muddy so will be left to dry for a week before being put over the cleaner/grader and into boxes.

Off for a long weekend in North Wales with Tracey, Moose, Carl, Sandra and that smoothie Labrador Jake. We are going on a barge of all things so I'm not really certain if it's such a good idea. Once again I have to share the back of the old boy's estate car with Jake which is somewhat trying as he does not like my boisterous disposition, preferring to spend the whole journey sleeping.

Get to our destination and there must be a total of 40 or 50 barges moored up as it is nearing the end of the season. Park up the car and unload our belongings into this luxury barge which will sleep eight people, so it seems Jake and I will have a room each rather than us having to share.

Pep talk by the owner – no speeding, no ramming other barges, no drinking while in charge of the boat and please return it in clean condition. As soon as he leaves we start up and set off. Most odd thing to drive – instead of a steering wheel you have this long handle called a tiller and to make things even more difficult, to turn right you push the handle to the left and vice-versa.

I'm not too partial to all this water but it really is quite peaceful, that is until I see dogs being taken for a walk along the towpath, and want to have a scrap with Jake and myself.

We come to this lock which means we all unload, except Carl who is the pilot, and the rest of us have this key to close the gates behind the barge and then slowly open the gates in front to let the water out and the barge then drops to the correct level, pulls forward and we close the second gate.

Every few hours we pause alongside a pub to stop for some nosh, and liquid refreshment, but in my case I stick to the coke, in case I end up falling in the water.

The next stage of our trip means going along this aqueduct with just a few inches each side of the barge – only a wall on the one side and a metre-wide path on the other side with a low wall and handrail alongside.

When we are only halfway across the barge comes to a stop even though the engine is still going, so Tracey, Moose and myself are pulling this barge along by a rope which is really hard work. I make the mistake of looking over the side and there is a sheer drop to a playing field below where a game is in progress. Those last two cokes and a pork pie were not such a good idea as I throw up over the crowded end of the field.

We get to the end of the aqueduct and mention to a walker our problem who suggests we try going in reverse, to free whatever is wrapped around the propeller which works. Away we go on our next leg of the journey before mooring for the night alongside another pub.

It really is a relaxing time on one of these canal holidays, with only the sound of the water lapping against the boat at night. During the day I can jump off the boat and walk alongside on the footpath. All too soon our break comes to an end and it's back home to Faulty Farm.

Sheep producers in areas free of Foot and Mouth for three months or more have just received the green light from Brussels to resume the lamb export trade. It is now up to the UK Government to put legislation in place to restart these exports.

This ending of export restrictions is good news because not only will it give a boost to prices but also to morale. Figures for October show the average price for lamb in the 12-21.5 kg weight range had fallen to 142.7p/kg dead-weight. This is more than 15 per cent down on last year's figure.

Marvellous news today for us canines who feared there would be a ban on hunting with dogs. Foxhunting will resume next month after being banned across much of Britain during the Foot and Mouth crisis. All forms of hunting with dogs, apart from deer hunting, should be allowed in disease free counties from 17th December. Plans to licence each meet and make hunts responsible for the activities of animal rights activists and saboteurs who try to disrupt them caused an outcry.

Because the danger of spreading foot and mouth remains, deer hunting will remain banned because of the wide chase area covered by the sport.

Foot and Mouth has changed the way of life for thousands of farmers, and not necessarily for the worse. Isolation and lack of information have driven them into the arms of the internet – and more than half are now online, which is a far cry from the popular image of the country bumpkin. In fact, usage increased by 69 per cent during the Foot and Mouth crisis, with the net becoming the main source of information.

The Gaffer is still trying to master the complexities of using a computer but really it's a bit of a lost cause – he's just too damn thick. The part that really gets up my nose is the name given to that object that darts all around the table – a mouse of all things.

British fruit growers are being forced to turn quality apples into juice at below the cost of production due to huge import tonnages. Despite an excellent harvest this year, supermarkets are continuing to source up to 70 per cent of their apples and pears from abroad. This dominance of imports is putting a question mark over the survival of many English varieties and will only speed up a process which has seen half of the English orchards grubbed out since 1970.

Switching to organic production has always been heralded as one of the ways British farmers can break out of the low profit trap of mainstream farming. But the premiums for organic production have only existed as long as demand exceeded supply. However, British producers can only meet a quarter of our organic needs, so overseas producers are rushing to fill the void.

The Soil Association says Britain must provide continuing support for organic farmers similar to that offered by EU states, instead of just subsidising them to convert. Even though the overall market is blossoming, most organic farmers desperately need additional support. Organic farming is the most developed form of sustainable agriculture and delivers environmental and health benefits with high standards of animal welfare.

The liveweight gains of the turkeys is still giving us cause for concern with one batch about two pounds lighter than they should be, so now most batches are on purchased pellets in a bid to speed them up.

We are convinced that the one batch of underperformers are of a smaller breed than we ordered but obviously we have no way of proving it. Another contributing factor is the continuing mild weather which means the birds are not eating so much feed, even so we still seem to spend a fair proportion of our time feeding them.

We have also started pressure washing buildings and cold rooms and doing maintenance work on machines in readiness for people's Christmas dinners.

The Gaffer always enjoys the run-up to Christmas as he says it's his pay-day. In fact at the moment he's going around here singing and whistling as if he hasn't a care in the world. I feel like saying to him to start acting his age – but if he did that he'd probably be dead.

The in-lamb ewes have just had their pre-lambing vaccination of 8 in 1 vaccine to provide immunity to their unborn lambs against clostridial disease. The two senior stock rams – Jim and Adam, were also treated. Jim was treated twice, after he attacked the Gaffer after the first treatment.

The woodlands of Britain are staging a remarkable comeback, according to a 'Doomsday Book' of trees. Within 20 years, there should be more woodland than when William the Conqueror ordered the first count in 1086, when woodland cover was 15 per cent. By 1900 the proportion had fallen to below 5 per cent.

By Tudor Times huge areas of woodland began to be slashed down. Britain was by now a great sea power, and there was an enormous demand for timber for shipbuilding for over two centuries.

During the 18th century, more timber was needed to build churches and buildings being established in the growing towns. In Sherwood Forest, some of the greatest oak trees were cut down to provide the roof timbers for St Paul's Cathedral in London. Vast amounts of oak were felled in the late 18th and early 19th centuries to provide bark for tanning leather. The furnaces of the Industrial Revolution were initially fuelled by charcoal, and much of the country was farmed so that by 1900, just 5 per cent of the country was tree-covered.

A great deal of timber was felled to meet the demands of the two World Wars and many acres were later cleared to provide food for the nation, but now, at long last the situation is being reversed. There are currently 25 trees for every person in the UK and oaks have become the UK's most common tree.

The 'Intervention Board' which for decades has been responsible for farmers being paid their farming subsidies, has just been replaced by the 'Rural Payments Agency' with promises of less red tape and quicker payments. However, within days of this revolutionary new department being set up the staff have gone on strike, and have already cost the Agency 'several thousand man days.'

This will mean that our IACS cheques will probably arrive even later than in previous years. DEFRA faces stiff fines from the EU if it fails to make payments to 96 per cent of eligible farmers by the end of January.

The closure of livestock markets this year should have enabled abattoirs and companies who trade direct on a dead weight basis to have increased their market share for the future. However, the exact reverse has happened because of their greed. Because so many producers – especially of lamb – have been penalised so heavily many will never sell their stock this way again. In fact, it looks as if next year will see record numbers of stock sold through live auction markets.

Some financial experts are predicting that the economic fortunes of farmers is likely to improve starting from early next year, due to the Euro exchange rate. At present the Euro is worth 62p but by this time next year it is predicted to be as high as 67p, giving farmers up to 10 per cent extra money for their products.

We have also been extremely bad at marketing in the UK giving the middleman ideal opportunities to make vast profits at our expense.

As an example, the retail price of milk in the UK is actually higher than in the Netherlands but the farmer's price is 20 per cent lower.

I nearly had Scampi for lunch today – well not really, Scampi is the name of a rather gorgeous young collie bitch I met up with in North Wales. The Gaffer, Missus and I went up there to see a flock of in-lamb pedigree ewes that were being dispersed. We have decided to increase our sheep numbers in possible readiness for quitting dairying in a few years' time. At the moment the margin from milk is absolutely pathetic, and with everyone increasing cow numbers to create a surplus of milk, the prospects do not appear favourable.

The drive up is one of completely contrasting countryside and farming systems. From Builth Wells to Newtown it is almost entirely sheep with a few suckler cows and the chances of diversification, except to B&B, are indeed quite limited. From Newtown to Welshpool we passed some superb large dairy farms with dead level extremely fertile land who could produce quality milk as efficiently as anywhere in the UK. From Welshpool to Llanfyllin and Lake Vyrnwy again we are back to sheep and cattle land, but all very neat and farmed to a high standard.

Anyway, these ewes we go to look at are scanned in lamb, have been sponged and lamb to AI rams in the middle of January. The couple who own them seem quite affluent – they have fruit on the table and no one is ill. After much haggling and looking at sheets of paper and Pedigree slips, a deal is done, and in a week's time Gareth will drive up with the Land Rover and stock trailer to collect an extra 32 ewes.

On the way home the Gaffer starts singing, which is just unbearable. The Missus manages to sleep through most of it but I was not so fortunate.

With the present state of farming, we seem to be having a serious problem with begging letters. However, we have decided to keep sending them.

One of our neighbours is building a ménage and Gareth and I are spending quite some time there with the telescopic handler. It really is a complicated procedure. First of all the whole area is levelled, then drained, and covered by a membrane which must not be damaged. Gareth then spreads 4 inches of stone all over with the loader, then another membrane is laid and this is covered by six inches of sand and then a thin layer of rubber chippings.

There are two terriers who live there called Rats and Cats, after their own speciality, so the three of us have several hunting sessions in an adjoining area of woodland. At the far end of this wood is an area of Christmas trees and we came across three poachers quietly sawing down trees which they obviously intend pinching. We decide there is not too much we can do about it, but we manage to find their lunch bags and eat all their sandwiches – very nice they were too.

Fears that Britain could be heading for a Christmas milk shortage have been ended by latest figures released by the dairy industry. This extra output is the result of the best Autumn for 40 years, stimulating grass growth, and high quality silage due to almost ideal growing conditions earlier in the Summer. So at the moment there is very little hope of a rise in the price of our milk.

Scientists are now claiming that up to 1,500 sheep could have been infected by BSE at the height of the epidemic. They claim it is vital that breeding techniques are changed so animals resistant to the disease can be introduced into the food chain. The disease has never been found in sheep but the threat to the national flock still exists.

Farmers have been failed by the people in charge. They should have been helped to form co-operatives for marketing and to keep their own costs down. Instead we've been too busy cutting our own throats to see what's been coming up behind us. And now it's here it's too late. The rest of the world has got its act together and Britain hasn't.

And it's easy to see what will happen next. The supermarkets will eliminate small growers and small shopkeepers until they control all the retail market, and then they will turn on each other. This will last for a while before they realise that there's no point, so they organise a cartel to increase their profits. At this stage the consumer really will be at their mercy because they will be able to charge whatever they like.

An absolute disaster happened here at Faulty Farm last night – a fox got into one of the turkey sheds and a total of 57 birds are either dead or had to be destroyed.

We've been having a tidy up recently and had stacked a load of pallets against the shed and Reynard had got on top of the pallets and into a hole that seemed hardly big enough for a cat. As the Missus and I were going around the turkey sheds first thing in the morning we sensed straight away by the noise and feathers inside the building that something was seriously wrong. Anyway the damn fox was still in there, so I gave chase – he jumped on a pallet in the corner of the shed and back out through the hole which was about 8 foot off the ground.

I took off in pursuit but did not really see him for dust. Back inside the shed was one of the worst cases of wanton destruction imaginable, with dead and wounded birds everywhere, and the remainder of the birds so frightened they will not gain any weight for at least a week. Also with only just over two weeks to the start of killing, the bruising will not have time to disappear so many more birds will be rejected.

The birds in this particular shed were all over 18 lb. in weight so we have a total loss of over £1,000 and we may have to buy in extra birds for our customers. We spend the entire morning collecting dead birds and humanely destroying anything injured and burying them. We also fill in the gap in the side of the building which incidentally has been there since the shed was built 10 years ago.

We manage to borrow a fox trap in the hope of catching him if he pays a return visit. The whole of our yard and surrounding area is floodlit which used to be a sufficient deterrent but not any more it seems.

Some of the loonies who think that foxes are nice kind furry animals and do no harm whatsoever, should have paid us a visit today to have had their eyes opened.

Gareth and a certain gorgeous young lady he is going out with go up to North Wales to collect the new sheep now that the Movement Licence has arrived. I was going to go along with them, but quite honestly I did not really have the time.

When the sheep are unloaded they seem to be bigger than we initially thought, so we are quite pleased with them.

December

We have now been two months since the last reported case of Foot and Mouth in the UK, and even though markets are still closed, there is much more movement of livestock occurring. Lorries and stock trailers carrying tack sheep to their Winter grazing are now a very common sight. The price of fat lamb is now in excess of £2.00 per kilo which is a great improvement on a month ago.

Our dairy cows are now housed night and day, but were out by day until the end of November which is probably the latest ever. All our beef and store cattle are also housed.

Even though the weather is becoming progressively wetter, it is still remarkably mild considering we are only three weeks away from the shortest day of the year. Even the moles seem to be fooled by the mild weather – mole heaps are suddenly appearing everywhere, whereas you don't normally see them until the beginning of January.

Today is 3rd December and an announcement that the whole of Wales and large parts of the UK are now classed as Foot and Mouth free, but we do still need licences for the movement of livestock.

A chart arrives in the post today of different colours, so perhaps we are going to splash some paint around and start to tart the place up, but the colours do seem somewhat drab, being all browns and grey. Outside goes the Gaffer with this chart and you will not believe it, but the silly git is virtually down on his hands and knees in the cow cubicles. This chart apparently tells you if the ration being fed to the cows is too high or low in protein, and too high or low in energy by looking at the colour of the dung. He comes to the conclusion that the ration is high in energy and low in protein, but he probably realised that anyway.

The Food Standards Agency are saying that we need an overhaul of the Dairy Industry with the milk being pasteurised for 25 seconds plus (instead of the 15-20 seconds at present) to kill off harmful bugs that reputedly cause a bowel disorder in humans called Crohn's disease. This is probably another cost that will be passed back to the producer meaning an excuse for another price reduction.

Britain's Farmers' Markets – all established in the last three years – have been the inspiration for farmers to move into the retail sector, claiming some of the profits which were previously creamed off by processors and supermarkets.

Farmers' markets have brought producers and consumers face to face, often for the first time, helping farmers understand shoppers' changing needs – and realise that many of these can be met straight from the farm.

We have been warned for the last five years that, unless we start to add value to basic commodities we will be unable to survive in a cut-throat global market. Consumer demand for prepared and speciality foods is being met by those who slice, dice and pre-pack fruit and vegetables, turn milk into ice-cream and cheese, and carry out on-farm butchery.

Chairman of the Food Standards Agency, Sir John Knebs, has said the bread industry should be congratulated on its contribution to people's diets. It has lowered salt levels in bread by more than a fifth in just three years to help combat heart disease.

Scientists have discovered why sheep appear to glow in the twilight hours. They say it is not merely a trick of the light but the result of natural fluorescence which can also be seen in blossom on trees. If you believe that you will believe anything. I don't ever recall seeing the sheep at this place glowing in the twilight hours. The Gaffer may start glowing if the sheep have escaped, but never the sheep.

A glut of organic milk is threatening to force prices down and put farmers out of business. There are fewer than 350 organic dairy farmers in Britain, producing around 400 million litres a year. However, around half is failing to find a market as only 4 per cent of shoppers regularly fill their baskets with organic goods. The rest is sold as standard milk for which producers receive less than 20p a litre compared with almost 30p for organic.

Livestock markets could be back in business by February, as part of a package of further relaxations to the Foot and Mouth movement restrictions currently being discussed between DEFRA and the Farming Unions.

The measures are being put together in the expectation that the last remaining F&M 'at risk' areas in the North of England will be officially declared free once the final blood tests are completed, some time in January. DEFRA officials have been at pains to stress that they do represent a further refinement of the existing controls, and should not be seen as a permanent regime.

Although the final details have still to be negotiated, it is already clear that markets will only be allowed to operate subject to strict controls. Buildings, concrete and penning must be in a condition to allow effective cleaning and disinfecting, cattle and sheep must be kept separate, only suitably attired market staff can handle animals, and everyone present will be expected to wear Wellingtons and clean outer clothing.

The resumption will apply to all types of cattle, but only to sheep and lambs going to slaughter. Sales of store and breeding sheep at market will remain banned for a further period. However, the 21 day standstill will remain in force, so as to limit the risk of Foot and Mouth spreading, should the disease return. This could cause problems if unsold animals have to be brought back from market.

As from 17th December multiple pick-ups will be allowed for over 30 month cattle *en route* to slaughter, making life easier for smaller farmers.

Scientists are this week claiming they have a quicker and equally reliable test for checking for Foot and Mouth disease. This test gives the result in two to three hours compared to three to four days previously, which must be very welcome news.

The Government has banned Egyptian potatoes from the end of November as 0.2 per cent of the 27,500 tons imported were infected with Potato Brown Rot Disease. If it can ban potatoes coming into the UK, surely it can ban illegal imports of meat from known infected countries, so reducing the risk of another outbreak of Foot and Mouth disease which would completely finish off UK agriculture as we know it.

Have had a refrigeration engineer here to 'gas-up' and check over all the cold rooms and refrigerated lorry containers ready for the turkey killing. We need a new motor in one cold room to get it running properly, otherwise all is OK. This year we have a different company to last year, which ended up sending us a complete dipstick who nearly caused us to lose ever so many birds.

Even though we still have our baited fox cage ready for the return of Reynard, so far he has eluded capture. Until we start killing, we cannot really tell how many birds will still be bruised after their skirmish, but we are expecting there to be at least 30 or 40 which we will end up selling as portions rather than whole birds.

The entire yard area here is now floodlit and also alarmed which sets off a siren. Before going in at night Sooty – the farm cat, and her offspring are shut into a cot to avoid triggering the alarms. However, a few stray cats cause me to lose much beauty sleep.

The in-lamb ewes and Jim and Adam are still on some off-lying land, but have just been moved to some fresh pasture with an abundance of grass and also plenty of high energy feed blocks. They start lambing in less than a month but until the turkeys have gone they cannot come home.

A very kind neighbour is looking at them twice a day in case any get on their backs and have their eyes pecked out by the crows. Once we start turkey killing we will not have a chance to see them during daylight hours ourselves.

The Consumers Association says European farm policies should be scrapped because they are helping to push up the price of food. They say the 50-year-old system of subsidised farming means that the same basket of food items which costs £84.65 here can be bought for £39.48 in New Zealand.

Food subsidies were scrapped overnight in New Zealand in the mid-1980s, when they accounted for 40 per cent of farm incomes. Since then farmers have met the challenge by increasing productivity and the sector has strengthened.

Now the Consumers Association says the time has come to do the same in Europe, where shoppers are rapidly losing faith in the policy's ability to deliver safe and healthy foods. It says the CAP costs a family of four £16 a week in hidden taxes, puts 2 pence on the rate of income tax, leads to intensive farming damaging the countryside and makes EU food probably the dearest in the world.

Farm Assured livestock now command a base price and non-Farm Assured are penalised. With more and more farms going organic, and within a very short time a surplus of organic livestock, the base price will be organic and the remainder penalised.

As always at this time of year some crackpot protest groups come up with video nasties of so called barbaric conditions under which Christmas turkeys are being reared. If we really reared birds under these conditions they would not be saleable and we would go bankrupt. When challenged to reveal their evidence for a police and RSPCA investigation, they declined so it was all a complete sham, as most of us knew all along.

One of the latest EU directives being discussed in Brussels concerning animal welfare says that it is cruel for cattle or sheep to be isolated, due to their natural herd or flock instinct. Presumably this means if you take a sheep to the vet for, let's say, a Caesarean operation, you have to take another one along for company. Furthermore when the one is being operated on, you need a third sheep to keep the one in the stock trailer company. Do you ever get the feeling that the world is going completely mad?

We've just been able to deliver our wool for sale which is a pleasant surprise. Six months ago we were being told it may not be saleable if you had been under Form D restrictions, as we ourselves were for 13 weeks.

Today we have a young farmer from Scotland arriving who is going to stay for two or three days and then decide if he comes here to work for a year prior to Agricultural College. His name is Angus, he has a mop of ginger hair and such a broad accent that I have difficulty understanding what he is saying.

He is quite a well educated lad, but is really green when it comes to practical farming – I'm just wondering if the Gaffer will have the patience to tolerate him. It will probably all be down to money – if the old boy can get away with paying a lower wage then he can afford the time to teach him and they will both benefit.

When he goes up the village for a pint in the evening he wears a kilt – which must be a real bird-puller in South East Wales.

He stays for several days and the whole family get on really well with him so he has decided to spend 12 months working here, starting early in the New Year.

It's now a really hectic few days leading up to the start of turkey killing – coats of paint in killing, cleaning and dressing rooms, cleaning and disinfecting cold rooms and shelving and countless other tasks.

The day before we start killing, the birds are driven around to a holding / catching shed – if they are not moved until the morning of killing they will be still tensed up and not pluck properly.

The 15th December and we start killing – the plucking machine, flight pullers, wing finishers etc. are going by 7.45, ready for the 'cleaners' who arrive at 8 o'clock.

We need to average ever-so-many birds per hour to get the task completed in eight days. This is easily achievable with small birds but can be quite difficult with larger birds or with bronze birds. A spare machine is kept for each operation as we cannot afford the time for a breakdown. A generator is run off a tractor as we are at the end of a line and do not have sufficient electricity power off the mains.

My main task is driving birds around ready for the next day's killing as well as the usual stock tasks of assisting with milking, scraping, calf rearing etc. By the second day we start turkey deliveries with the van so are on up to four or five loads a day. We end up going over the Severn Bridge with 10 loads as well as to local butchers, a delivery into Pembrokeshire of small long legged birds, a collection from Carmarthenshire of medium weight birds (dressed), and a collection of medium weight birds (live) from Worcestershire in the Land Rover and stock trailer. The reason for buying in so many medium weight birds is because we ourselves ended up with one batch being a smaller breed than we ordered.

The weather throughout the whole of turkey killing has been absolutely superb for the job with a slight frost every night and staying fairly cold by day which means that refrigeration for the birds is not so critical. We end up with 300 small birds not killed, and as Easter is early next year, we will keep them until then.

Heard on the radio about two women fighting in a supermarket over the last 18 lb. frozen turkey. If they'd only realized it was probably a two-year-old ex-layer that was pumped full of water, they may not have been so stupid. It never ceases to amaze me the rubbish some people will buy when home produced food is such good value.

Everyone's hands and wrists are swollen up from handling, carrying and dressing turkeys, but within 10 days it is all over and we sit down to turkey for Christmas dinner with a few bottles of Welsh wine to wash it down.

It really is such a contrast to only 24 hours previously when the yard was full of customers coming to collect their turkeys, the telephone going non-stop, running low on 14 lb. birds and having to juggle the weights around and making certain we did not run out of 17 lb. bronze birds. It is by far the most demanding of all our varied farming enterprises, and as you are on a strict timetable to have all the birds ready for Christmas Day, there is absolutely no room for error.

I can't help but get the feeling of discrimination against us canines. As an example, a car can park on the pavement dripping oil without reprimand but if a dog messes there, its owner is liable to a £1,000 fine. If a cat catches wildlife this is viewed as nature, if a dog does the same it is accused of being out of control – a possible death penalty. Pat a strange dog and he bites, another death penalty. Stroke a cat and it bites, you're told it's your own fault for stroking it.

The professors of epidemiology who came up with the 24 to 48 hour cull on contiguous farms within three kilometres of an outbreak got it badly wrong. True, some 2,000 farms had Foot and Mouth, but only five in 7,549 contiguous culls turned out to be infected with the disease, showing that spread was much slower than expected.

While everyone welcomes the end of F&M, are we not turning a blind eye to the fact that cattle have been untested for TB for 9 months? There will be a severe build-up of TB, particularly on the farms which should have been on annual testing. Allowing free movement from hotspot areas will simply spread TB far and wide. It will take a number of years to regain lost ground anyway, and this forgotten crisis is still out there.

Boxing Day and would you believe it, but we spend the entire day spud grading. Two lorry loads to go before 8 o'clock tomorrow morning but they are both regular customers and we cannot let them down or they will go elsewhere for the rest of the season.

The next day, and after milking, scraping, feeding and loading two lorries with spuds, we have a full day bringing in-lamb ewes home ready for lambing and also make a start cleaning turkey manure out of the buildings ready for housing the ewes.

It is now 30 years since the last stretch of the M4 motorway was completed, linking London to South Wales in only a few hours' drive. In its first year, there were an average of 20,000 vehicles a day using the motorway, and now there are 160,000 daily. I just dread to think of what it will be like in another 30 years' time.

Just 24 hours after bringing the ewes home Jack and Jill arrive – yes we've started lambing and by the look of the udders on some of the old dears many more will quickly follow. However, with the sheds being cleaned out they can stay inside if the weather breaks.

The weather incidentally has been near perfect for about the last 10 weeks with virtually no rain and mostly mild, with the result that the sheep are still running out as are most people's dry cows and many store cattle which means a big saving on feed and especially straw, which is very expensive.

The Gaffer says the last time we had a winter as dry as this was 1975-76 in which we had no rain virtually all winter and then the drought of 1976. However, if he is prophesying another drought 2002 will probably turn out to be the wettest year on record.

A very important new arrival today here at Faulty Farm – my son and heir, who is now over six months old, arrives here as my assistant and not before time too. He is already bigger than myself and so full of energy it just tires me out. For some reason he has been given the name Zero, but I suppose we'll get used to it. He comes complete with his own dog basket which is placed next to mine so we both have the privilege of sleeping in the house next to the fire. I tell him that the Missus and Gareth are an absolute pushover but the old boy can be difficult if he takes a dislike to you.

Today is 31st December and it is now three months since the last case of Foot and Mouth disease that has seen millions of animals slaughtered. Government officials could decide within a week whether to lift the at-risk status still covering Cumbria, North Yorkshire, Durham and Northumberland.

Any decision is dependent on the Chief Veterinary Officer, who must be satisfied the country is clear and more blood tests will continue in badly hit areas. We can only speculate on when a decision will be made to remove the restrictions on the farming community.

This last 12 months have been extremely traumatic for agriculture and rural businesses. Apart from the ravages of Foot and Mouth, and very low commodity prices causing severe financial problems, the Government has made absolutely no attempt to stop legal or illegal imports of meat from countries which have Foot and Mouth disease. So in a few years' time, we could experience the whole scenario once again.

I hope you have enjoyed sharing my memories of this last 12 months, and remember life is what you make it. Things don't just happen; you have to make them happen. Can't stop any longer – the Gaffer is shouting for me and my young lad Zero to help him catch a ewe that is lambing.

Goodbye and God bless you all.